American Red Cross
Advanced Child Care Training

Handbook

American Red Cross

This handbook is part of the American Red Cross Advanced Child Care Training program. By itself, it does not constitute complete and comprehensive training. Visit redcross.org to learn more about this program.

The emergency care procedures outlined in this book reflect the standard of knowledge and accepted emergency practices in the United States at the time this book was published. It is the reader's responsibility to stay informed of changes in emergency care procedures.

The infection control procedures outlined in this book reflect the current standards and guidelines of the Centers for Disease Control (CDC) and Occupational Safety and Health Administration (OSHA) in the United States at the time this book was published. Because regulations influencing these standards and guidelines change frequently and because laws are redefined, it is the reader's responsibility to stay current with information such as infection control by attending in-service courses offered by employers or through other sources.

The enclosed materials, including all content, graphics, images and logos, are copyrighted by and the exclusive property of the American National Red Cross ("Red Cross"). Unless otherwise indicated in writing by the Red Cross, the Red Cross grants you ("recipient") the limited right to receive and use the printed materials, subject to the following restrictions:

- The recipient is prohibited from reproducing the materials for any reason.

- The recipient is prohibited from creating electronic versions of the materials.

- The recipient is prohibited from revising, altering, adapting or modifying the materials.

- The recipient is prohibited from creating any derivative works incorporating, in part or in whole, the content of the materials.

Any rights not expressly granted herein are reserved by the Red Cross. The Red Cross does not permit its materials to be reproduced or published without advance written permission from the Red Cross. To request permission to reproduce or publish Red Cross materials, please submit your written request to the American National Red Cross.

Published by Krames StayWell Strategic Partnerships Division

Printed in the United States of America

ISBN: 978-1-58480-599-1

Acknowledgments

Many individuals shared in the development process of the American Red Cross Advanced Child Care Training program in various supportive, technical and creative ways. This program was made possible through the dedication of employees, volunteers, and trusted professionals. Their commitment to excellence is sincerely appreciated.

The staff of the American Red Cross

The staff of Krames StayWell Strategic Partnerships Division

The staff of SealWorks Interactive Studios

The staff of ZoDev Studios

The staff of Portfolio Productions

Our subject matter experts, including:

David C. Berry, PhD, ATC, ATRIC, CKTP

Jonathan L. Epstein, MEMS, NREMT-P

S. Robert Seitz, MEd, RN, NREMT-P

Susan K. Carman, MSN, MBA

John Harrell, AAS, EMT-P

Nancy T. Hatfield, RN, BSN, MAE

Debra Holtzman, JD, MA

Terri Kyle, MSN, CPNP

Cynthia "Cutter" Martin

Lisa McClellan

Dana Stair, RN

Special thanks to The American Red Cross Scientific Advisory Council

The American Red Cross Scientific Advisory Council is a panel of nationally recognized experts in emergency medicine, sports medicine, emergency medical services (EMS), emergency preparedness, disaster mobilization and other public health and safety fields. The Council helps ensure that Red Cross courses, training materials and products incorporate the latest scientific and technical information.

The American Red Cross would like to extend a very special thank you to the families who graciously opened their homes to us to film the video associated with this program.

Contents

CHAPTERS

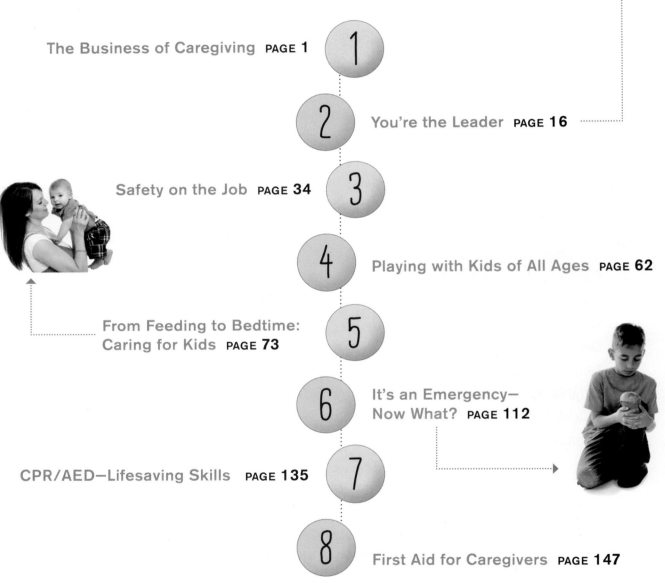

The Business of Caregiving **PAGE 1** — 1

2 — You're the Leader **PAGE 16**

Safety on the Job **PAGE 34** — 3

4 — Playing with Kids of All Ages **PAGE 62**

From Feeding to Bedtime: Caring for Kids **PAGE 73** — 5

6 — It's an Emergency— Now What? **PAGE 112**

CPR/AED—Lifesaving Skills **PAGE 135** — 7

8 — First Aid for Caregivers **PAGE 147**

Appendix A **Activity Sheets** • Appendix B **Sample Forms for Caregivers**
Appendix C **Fun Activities for Kids** • Appendix D **First Aid Emergencies from A to Z**

Detailed Contents

Chapter 1: The Business of Caregiving 1

First Things First! 2

Marketing Yourself 4

SUCCESS! I'm Hired! Now What? 8

Building Your Business 14

Chapter 2: You're the Leader 16

Leading the Way 17

What to Do When Children Misbehave 24

Chapter 3: Safety on the Job 34

Staying Safe at Home 35

Staying Safe While You Are Out and About 37

Staying Safe During a Weather Event 44

Staying Safe from House Fires 48

Preventing Accidental Injuries 50

Chapter 4: Playing with Kids of All Ages 62

Play: It's a Tough Job 63

Types of Play 64

How to Play with Kids 65

Play It Safe 71

Chapter 5: From Feeding to Bedtime: Caring for Kids 73

Following Care Routines 74

Watching Out for Germs 74

Handling a Crying Baby 77

Picking Up and Holding Children 81

Feeding Children 83

Giving Medications 90

Changing Diapers and Helping with the Potty 92

Dressing Children 94

Bathing Children 95

Brushing and Flossing a Child's Teeth 95

Good Night, Good Morning! 96

Skill Sheet 5-1: Hand Washing 99

Skill Sheet 5-2: Removing Disposable Gloves 100

Skill Sheet 5-3: Picking Up an Infant 101

Skill Sheet 5-4: Holding an Infant 102

Skill Sheet 5-5: Picking Up and Holding a Toddler 103

Skill Sheet 5-6: Bottle-Feeding 104

Skill Sheet 5-7: Spoon-Feeding 106

Skill Sheet 5-8: Diapering 108

Skill Sheet 5-9: Helping a Child Put On and Take Off a Shirt 110

Chapter 6: It's an Emergency–Now What? _____ 112

Being Prepared _____ 113

Responding to First Aid Emergencies _____ 118

To Move or Not to Move? _____ 128

Skill Sheet 6-1: Checking a Conscious Child _____ 131

Skill Sheet 6-2: Checking an Unconscious Child _____ 133

Chapter 7: CPR/AED–Lifesaving Skills _____ 135

Background _____ 136

Cardiac Emergencies _____ 136

Breathing Emergencies and Unconscious Choking _____ 141

Skill Sheet 7-1: CPR–Child (Older Than 1 Year) _____ 142

Skill Sheet 7-2: CPR–Infant _____ 144

Skill Sheet 7-3: Using an AED _____ 146

Chapter 8: First Aid for Caregivers _____ 147

Breathing Emergencies _____ 148

Sudden Illness _____ 153

Environmental Emergencies _____ 160

Soft Tissue Injuries _____ 167

Muscle, Bone and Joint Injuries _____ 170

Skill Sheet 8-1: Assisting with an Asthma Inhaler _____ 176

Skill Sheet 8-2: Conscious Choking–Child (Older Than 1 Year) _____ 177

Skill Sheet 8-3: Conscious Choking–Infant _____ 178

Skill Sheet 8-4: Unconscious Choking–Child (Older Than 1 Year) _____ 179

Skill Sheet 8-5: Unconscious Choking–Infant _____ 180

Skill Sheet 8-6: Taking a Temperature _____ 182

Skill Sheet 8-7: Assisting with an Epinephrine Auto-Injector _____ 184

Skill Sheet 8-8: Controlling Severe Bleeding _____ 185

Skill Sheet 8-9: Applying a Soft Splint _____ 186

Skill Sheet 8-10: Applying a Rigid Splint _____ 187

Skill Sheet 8-11: Applying an Anatomic Splint _____ 188

Skill Sheet 8-12: Applying a Sling _____ 189

Appendices

Appendix A – Activity Sheets _____ 190

Appendix B – Sample Forms for Caregivers _____ 210

Appendix C – Fun Activities for Kids _____ 231

Appendix D – First Aid Emergencies from A to Z _____ 239

Sources _____ 278

Photo Credits _____ 283

Index _____ 286

Health Precautions During First Aid Training

The American Red Cross has trained millions of people in first aid, CPR and AED using manikins as training aids. The Red Cross follows widely accepted guidelines for cleaning and decontaminating training manikins. If these guidelines are adhered to, the risk of any kind of disease transmission during training is extremely low.

To help minimize the risk of disease transmission, you should follow some basic health precautions and guidelines while participating in training. You should take additional precautions if you have a condition that would increase your risk or other participants' risk of exposure to infections. Request a separate training manikin if you:

- Have an acute condition, such as a cold, sore throat or cuts or sores on your hands or around your mouth.

- Know that you are seropositive (have had a positive blood test) for hepatitis B surface antigen (HBsAg), which indicates that you are currently infected with the hepatitis B virus.*

- Know that you have a chronic infection as indicated by long-term seropositivity (long-term positive blood tests) for HBsAg* or a positive blood test for anti-HIV, that is, a positive test for antibodies to human immunodeficiency virus (HIV), the virus that causes many severe infections, including acquired immunodeficiency syndrome (AIDS).

- Have had a positive blood test for hepatitis C virus.

- Have a type of condition that makes you extremely likely to get an infection.

To obtain information about testing for individual health status, go to the Centers for Disease Control and Prevention website (cdc.gov).

After a person has had an acute hepatitis B infection, he or she will no longer test positive for HBsAg but will test positive for the hepatitis B antibody (anti-HBs). People who have been vaccinated against hepatitis B will also test positive for anti-HBs. A positive test for anti-HBs should not be confused with a positive test for HBsAg.

If you decide that you should have your own manikin, ask your instructor if he or she can provide one for you. You will not be asked to explain why you make this request. The manikin will not be used by anyone else until it has been cleaned according to the recommended end-of-class decontamination procedures. Because the number of manikins available for class use is limited, the more advance notice you give, the more likely it is that you can be provided a separate manikin.

*People with hepatitis B infection will test positive for HBsAg. Most people infected with hepatitis B virus will get better in time. However, some hepatitis B infections will become chronic and linger for much longer. People with these chronic infections will continue to test positive for HBsAg. Their decision to participate in CPR training should be guided by their physician.

Guidelines

In addition to taking the precautions regarding manikins, you can protect yourself and other participants from infection by following these guidelines:

- Wash your hands thoroughly before participating in class activities.

- Do not eat, drink, use tobacco products or chew gum during class when manikins are used.

- Clean the manikin properly before use.

- For some manikins, cleaning properly means vigorously wiping the manikin's face and the inside of its mouth with a clean gauze pad soaked with either a fresh solution of liquid chlorine bleach and water (¼ cup of sodium hypochlorite per gallon of tap water) or rubbing alcohol. The surfaces should remain wet for at least 1 minute before they are wiped dry with a second piece of clean, absorbent material.

- For other manikins, cleaning properly means changing the manikin's face. Your instructor will provide you with instructions for cleaning the type of manikin used in your class.

- Follow the guidelines provided by your instructor when practicing skills such as clearing a blocked airway with your finger.

Physical Stress and Injury

Successful course completion requires full participation in classroom and skill sessions, as well as successful performance during skill and knowledge evaluations. Because of the nature of the skills in this course, you will participate in strenuous activities, such as performing CPR on the floor. If you have a medical condition or disability that will prevent you from taking part in the skill practice sessions, please tell your instructor so that accommodations can be made.

If you are unable to participate fully in the course, you may audit the course and participate as much as you can or desire but you will not be evaluated. To participate in the course in this way, you must tell the instructor before training begins. Be aware that you will not be eligible to receive a course completion certificate.

THE BUSINESS OF CAREGIVING

So, you've given it some thought, and you think caregiving might be a good way for you to earn spending money for special purchases, extra income for living or school expenses or even a steady, reliable income to support yourself. You may be in college or just starting out in the workforce. You may have young children and want to stay home with them, or grown children and lots of extra time. The idea of a part- to full-time job with flexible hours sounds good to you. You like kids, and kids like you. You're responsible, reliable and trustworthy. This could be the perfect job for you! Let's take a closer look at how you can get your caregiving business started and keep it running smoothly.

First Things First!

Before you start lining up caregiving jobs, it pays to spend a little time thinking about what skills and qualifications you need to work as a caregiver, what expectations parents have, what types of caregiving jobs you want and what types of caregiving jobs you are best suited for.

Skills and Qualifications

Parents who are looking for a reliable, mature caregiver expect a certain level of skills and qualifications. In today's busy world, many parents want to hire a caregiver who is capable of feeding, bathing, dressing and/or transporting their children to school, daycare, sports, lessons and activities. Many want to hire caregivers who will play with their children and also help them with homework. All of these responsibilities require a high level of knowledge, safety and skill. The good news is that by taking this caregiving training course, you will learn what it takes to be a great caregiver, *and* you will receive training and certification in pediatric first aid/CPR.

In addition to certification in pediatric first aid/CPR, some parents may be looking for caregivers who have a valid driver's license and/or caregivers with swimming and water safety training. Finding certified courses in swimming and water safety is easy. Simply go to www.redcross.org, plug in your zip code, and a list of available courses will pop up. Check your local and state laws to find out if any other certifications or documents are needed.

Parent Expectations

It is important to know that some parents may require you to undergo different types of background checks in addition to submitting several references before they hire you for a caregiving job. Parents want to know that they are leaving their children in the care of a qualified professional who has a clean legal and driving record. Parents may also check social media sites for any display of inappropriate behavior. Make sure that your professional, legal and personal life is in order before applying for a caregiving job!

Types of Jobs

Opportunities abound for reliable, qualified caregivers. Parents are eager to find summer child care, part-time child care, full-time child care, live-in caregivers and even caregivers who will go with the family on a vacation. Think about the type of job you want and the type of job you can handle. For example, maybe you are pretty sure you can handle watching an older child before and after school,

Be Savvy About Social Media

Social media sites like Facebook and Twitter are fun, and they are a great way to let your friends and family know what you're up to and what you're into. But you need to be careful. Make sure the way you represent yourself on social media sites is the way you want the world to see you. Never post or tweet anything you will be ashamed of later, like mean-spirited or sarcastic comments or embarrassing or revealing photos. Some of the families you work for may friend you on Facebook or follow you on Twitter, and you don't want to give them any reason to think that you are immature or irresponsible!

In addition, don't post or tweet anything about your caregiving activities before, during or after the job. It may be tempting to post that you are looking forward to an upcoming caregiving job or to tweet a cute photo of the kids or mention the fun things you are doing with them in a status update. But, posting about your caregiving activities on social media sites is never a good idea. For one thing, information you share on social media is never entirely private. Anyone who clicks your status update can see where you are and what you are doing, and this isn't great when you are home alone with children. Why invite trouble? Also, be aware that many families may prefer that you don't post photos of their children on social media sites, and especially not without their permission. Out of courtesy to the family, and for your own safety and the safety of the kids, keep quiet about your caregiving activities on social media!

but you are are nervous about the thought of caring for a baby on a full-time, live-in basis. Think about the experience, personal qualities and skills that you will bring to the job. Perhaps you are a nursing student, certified in first aid/CPR, who worked with children with special needs during a clinical rotation. Maybe you raised three kids of your own, have a special talent for coming up with silly songs and games to keep kids amused and really know your way around a changing table. Perhaps you are the oldest sibling of five kids, two of whom have asthma. Completing the **Caregiver's Self-Assessment Tool** in Appendix B can help you determine what sorts of jobs are most within your comfort zone. As you gain more experience as a caregiver, your experience and comfort level will increase—so it's a good idea to use the Caregiver's Self Assessment Tool about every 6 months. You can also download this tool from your online course.

Marketing Yourself

Now that you are aware of the qualifications necessary to be a professional and marketable caregiver, and you have an idea about what kind of caregiving jobs you want, it's time to learn how to get the word out to potential customers.

Networking

One of the best ways to get caregiving jobs is by networking, or through word of mouth. Ask friends, classmates, neighbors, roommates, relatives and professors if they need a caregiver or if they know someone else who does. Talk to other caregivers and offer to fill in as a substitute. Parents would rather hire a caregiver they know, but the next best thing would be to hire a caregiver recommended by someone they trust. If your networking results in job offers from families you don't know, be sure to interview the family before accepting the job.

Business Cards

Business cards can be a very helpful tool for building up your caregiving business. You can make your own business cards using the **Business Card Template** found in your online course. You can also check out a sample in Appendix B. Give your business cards to families interested in hiring you. Ask friends, relatives and neighbors to give your cards to people they know who might need a caregiver. It is fine for you to give out your business cards to people you know and trust and to ask them to give your cards to people they know, but never advertise to the general public.

> One of the best ways to get caregiving jobs is by networking, or through word of mouth.

Ryan Smith

1204 Street Lane
New York, NY 11201
555-123-0123
rsmith92@gmail.com

Caregiving Services

BE SMART, BE SAFE! Do not post your name, address, phone number or e-mail address on the Internet. Only post your résumé and contact info on trusted job/career websites (see Online Caregiving Services section on page 7). Do not place your business cards, résumé or any other marketing materials (such as fliers) in coffee shops, grocery stores or other public places. It's unsafe to allow total strangers to get your name, address, phone number or e-mail address!

Caregiving for Military Families

If you live on or near a military base, many of your customers may be military families. In most ways, military families are no different than other families. What is special about military families is that a parent—and sometimes both parents—may be gone for long periods of time, often in distant, dangerous or unknown locations. This is called deployment. Deployment can be a stressful time for military families.

Deployment is stressful for all family members and it can affect children in many different ways. Feelings such as fear, worry, doubt, confusion, sadness, anger and guilt are very common. These feelings can cause the child to act differently than he or she normally would. For example, the child may have trouble sleeping; be cranky, sad or whiny; or seem very "clingy." Some children may lose interest in school or their friends, or become more aggressive. Preschoolers who have been potty trained for some time might go back to having accidents. Even babies may show behavior changes, such as refusing to eat.

Here's how you can help when you are caregiving for military families:

- Maintain regular routines.

- Give the kids extra attention, comfort (holding and hugging) and reassurance.

- Be patient and calm when a child is clingy, whiny or aggressive, but do not tolerate bad behavior. Children who misbehave need to have their behavior corrected.

- Don't avoid talking about the parent who is deployed. Encourage children to express their feelings about the deployment. If a child asks questions about the deployment, answer her questions with brief, to-the-point responses. This helps to prevent the child's imagination from taking over.

- Don't let the kids watch or listen to television or radio news reports of military conflicts.

- Help the kids make cards or a craft present to send to the parent who is deployed.

- Let the kids know that their parent is doing an important job.

Your Résumé

A résumé is another great tool for helping you get caregiving jobs. A résumé is a brief summary of your education, experience and skills. You can see an example of a caregiver's résumé in Appendix B. You should have a résumé ready to give to families interested in hiring you as their caregiver. The **Résumé Builder Tool** in your online course can help you create your own résumé.

When you are working on your résumé, don't worry if you don't have much professional experience caregiving yet. You can list courses you have taken (including this one!), certifications you have completed, life experiences you have had, other jobs you have held, volunteer work that you have done and activities that you participate in. You can list any experience you have caring for children. You may have children of your own; you may be the oldest child of several siblings; or you may be a mature parent with adult children. Even if your past experience doesn't involve caring for kids directly, it probably involves skills and qualities that you will use as a caregiver. Working at a store or restaurant while going to school shows that you are reliable, flexible and hardworking; it

requires you to balance work and studies, be on time and have a good attitude while serving a wide range of customer personalities. Playing on a sports team shows that you know how to work with other people to achieve a goal. And doing volunteer work shows that you are actively involved in your community and that you care about others.

Looking at the sample résumé in Appendix B, you can see that your résumé should also list references—people who are able to recommend you as a caregiver. When you think about people to ask to be a reference for you, think about people who know firsthand what your strengths are and what you will bring to the job. Families you have worked for in the past and who are happy with your work are great people to ask for references, but any adult who is not related to you and knows you well is a good choice. For example, a former employer, coach, teacher, scout leader or clergy member would also be able to recommend you on the basis of qualities such as reliability or your willingness to work hard. Before listing a person as a reference, always ask the person whether he or she would be willing to be a reference for you. Make sure the people who have agreed to be references for you know that you

have put them on your résumé and understand that they may get phone calls asking about you.

Get in the habit of updating your résumé every 6 months or so. As you gain more experience, you will want to make sure to showcase it!

Online Caregiving Services

A current trend in marketing yourself as a qualified caregiver is through safe, secure online caregiving sites. These types of sites are especially helpful for parents in high-stress jobs, military parents, parents who frequently move, or parents who live in a town or city far from their immediate families.

Staying Safe

As your caregiving business expands, you may start to work for families outside of your immediate circle of friends and relatives. For example, one of the families you work for regularly may recommend your caregiving services to another family that is looking for a good caregiver. Or you may be contacted about a job from a secure online caregiving site. When agreeing to meet for the first time with parents/families you do not know, be sure to arrange the meeting at a safe, public meeting place or take a friend or relative with you to the interview. Always trust your gut. If you get to a caregiving job and something makes you uncomfortable or you feel you are in danger for any reason, don't be afraid to tell the family that you have changed your mind, and leave. Get to know the families of the children you care for, and meet their pets. If caregiving for a certain family makes you feel uncomfortable, don't work for them again. And, as always, before leaving for any caregiving job, make sure a relative or friend knows where you will be, when to expect you home and how to contact you. Have some alternative means of transportation home available if you are not comfortable with a driver who has been arranged for you. Also be sure that you know how you can get in touch with your family or friends while you are caregiving.

The parents who use these secure websites are looking for qualified caregivers who are at least 18 years of age or older. Parents typically pay a fee to have access to potential caregivers' online résumés and to post their own job requests. As a caregiver looking for a job, you post your résumé on the site, the type of caregiving job for which you are looking and your availability. You do not post any personal contact information. However, the site makes it easy for interested parents to contact you if they would like to set up an interview.

SUCCESS! I'm Hired! Now What?

Before you accept a caregiving job, you need to meet with the family to discuss the job requirements. This meeting is the best way for the family to find out if you are right for the caregiving job and for you to find out if the job is right for you.

Use this meeting as an opportunity to meet the children you will be caregiving and to discuss important details about the job with the parents. You want to make sure that the job fits into your schedule and is within your comfort zone! Covering the following points will help you assess the job:

- **Date and time.** Find out what dates and times you'll be expected to work.

- **Length of time.** Long hours make the job harder and may interfere with your course work, family life, activities or another job. If you are new to caregiving, you might want to start out with shorter jobs that last only 1 or 2 hours a day.

- **Transportation.** How will you get to and from the job? Always make sure you have reliable transportation arrangements.

Making a Great Impression

During your meeting with the family, help them to see you as the responsible, personable person that you are. Make a great first impression by following these tips:

- Arrive on time or a few minutes early.

- Dress appropriately. Wear neat, clean clothes that are modest and do not have inappropriate slogans on them. Do not wear skirts or shorts that are too short, tops that are low cut or any clothing that shows your stomach.

- Brush your hair, and make sure your hands and fingernails are clean.

- Bring copies of your résumé and business cards.

- Be friendly and polite. Say "please" and "thank you." Maintain eye contact and nod your head to show that you are listening.

- Don't just sit there! Show your interest in the family and the job. Ask questions about the children and your responsibilities. Ask if you can meet the children and try to get to know them. Make sure you wash your hands before playing with or holding children, especially babies.

- Be sure to mention the American Red Cross caregiving training, certifications and qualifications you have completed. Professional certifications indicate that you take the job of caring for children very seriously and that you want to be a great caregiver!

- Be prepared and willing to talk about your experience and the special qualities and skills you can bring to the job. If you have experience caregiving, you can mention the number and types of caregiving jobs that you've had, including the children's ages and the hours you worked. You can also give parents a glimpse into your caregiving style by mentioning activities you have planned to do with the kids or by describing how you handled a difficult situation on the job. Even if you don't have experience caregiving, you can talk about other jobs you have held (paid or unpaid) and the experience you gained from them.

- Tell the family about your hobbies and interests.

- **Number of children.** Do not agree to care for more children than you can safely handle. For many caregivers, that means no more than three children. Use the Caregiver's Self-Assessment Tool to get an idea about how many kids you can safely handle. If there are too many children for you to safely care for, ask if you can bring along another caregiver to help. Before the job, make sure the other caregiver meets the family, and discuss payment and the details of the job with your "co-worker." If you have a friend work with you, remember your focus should be on the kids you are caregiving, not each other.

- **Ages of the children.** In general, younger children need more care. Caregiving jobs where you are expected to watch several young children (three or more) by yourself can be very challenging. Do not accept these jobs if you do not feel comfortable doing so. New caregivers should not take jobs involving a baby or more than one toddler until they have some experience.

- **Responsibilities.** Some families may ask you to do other chores like bathing a child or preparing meals. Do not accept any additional responsibilities unless you are qualified, willing and can do them safely.

Getting a Ride

Before accepting a caregiving job, make sure you know how you plan to get there and back. If you don't own a car, sometimes the family you are caregiving for will offer to give you a ride back home or they may offer you money for public transportation to and from the job. Make sure you discuss financial arrangements for transportation with the parents before accepting the job, including whether or not you will be reimbursed for gas money or cab or metro fare.

Always call a friend or family member when you are ready to leave the caregiving job to let them know you will be home soon. This is especially important if you are walking, riding your bike or taking some form of public transportation back home. Be very cautious if you must walk or ride your bike home at night. Be sure to wear visible clothing and stay on well-lit streets. It goes without saying that you should never accept a ride home from a stranger.

Family Values

Families are alike in many ways. In other ways, families are very different. As a caregiver, you may have the opportunity to work for families that are very different from your own or the one in which you were raised. Learn to appreciate these differences! When you are caregiving, you are a guest in the family's home. Always follow the family's rules, and respect their customs and preferences. You may find that the families you work for are different in the following ways:

- **Cultural differences.** If the family is from a different country or culture than your own, the family might speak with an accent, look different than you or dress in clothes that are unfamiliar. They might have different customs and ways of doing things. You can learn a lot from these families—about new foods, customs and holidays. This is also a fun way to learn new words.

- **Religious beliefs.** You may work for families with religious beliefs different from your own. The parents might give special instructions, such as "Make sure Alex says his prayers before bed" or "Since it is Friday, please make sure Britney doesn't eat meat."

- **Family income.** All families do not have the same amount of money to spend, and every family is different in how they choose to spend their money. The children you care for will have different kinds of toys and clothes and live in different homes and neighborhoods. Children can grow up happy and healthy no matter how much the family spends on clothes, toys, food and other things.

- **Family structure.** Families take many shapes. Many families are "traditional," with a mother, a father and one or more children. But it is just as common to see single-parent families, blended families (a family that includes children from one or more previous marriages), families with two moms or two dads, and families where the children are being raised by people who are not their natural parents (for example, grandparents raising grandchildren).

Always follow the family's rules, and respect their customs and preferences.

- **House rules.** Know the house rules for the children, and for you. For example, it is better to know if the children are allowed to play certain video games, go on the Internet (including what websites they are permitted to visit) or have dessert after dinner, before they tell you, "My mommy said I can!" You will also want to ask the parents about their expectations for you while you are in their home. For example, the parents may prefer that you not use certain pieces of electronic equipment or household appliances.

- **Children with special needs.** Some children with special needs may use equipment, like a wheelchair. Before caregiving a child with special needs, make sure the child's parents teach you how to provide any special care the child may need. Don't accept the caregiving job unless you feel 100 percent comfortable providing the care the child needs.

- **Pets.** Find out if the family has any pets, and meet them. Ask if they are friendly and if you are expected to care for them.

Come to the meeting prepared. Bring a copy of your résumé and a few of your business cards. Download the **Family Interview Form**, the **Parental Consent and Contact Form** and the **Family Emergency Information Card** in your online course and bring these along with you. You can also check out samples in Appendix B.

- The **Family Interview Form** will help you remember what to ask and gives you a place to write down the answers.

- The **Parental Consent and Contact Form** is a form that you should give to the parents and ask them to complete. This form is a place where the parents can detail any special care that their child requires. By signing this form, the parents give you permission to provide that care according to their instructions. The parents can also use this form to provide the names and contact information for an adult who can make decisions on the child's behalf if the parents cannot be reached.

- The **Family Emergency Information Card** is another form that you should have the parents fill out. This form captures basic, essential information that will be useful to have in case of an emergency.

Use all three of these forms for each new caregiving job. Even if you have worked for the family before, you should review the forms and update them with any new information each time.

BE SMART, BE SAFE! Bathing young children and taking children swimming are high-risk activities. Safety experts recommend certification in first aid/CPR if you are responsible for bathing young children or supervising children who are swimming or playing in or around water.

In case the family offers you a job, be prepared to discuss your rate and payment details. Politely tell them what you charge. For example, you could say, "Thank you for this opportunity Mr. and Mrs. Chilton. Before accepting the job I'd like to discuss my rate. I usually charge $14 per hour. Is that OK with you?" It's OK if a parent tries to negotiate a different rate with you; just remember that you can negotiate too. Figure out in advance how low you are willing to go. If a parent offers you a lower rate than you usually charge, you can counter with a different rate until you reach an agreement. Also, be sure to tell the family if you prefer to be paid in cash or if you will accept checks.

Before accepting any caregiving job, check your schedule for conflicts. You may not be able to take the job if you have class or another job scheduled. It's fine to tell the family that you will call them back to confirm once you check your schedule. Just remember to follow through! For example, if you tell the family that you will call them back later that day, be sure to do it.

Money Matters

You may be wondering how much to charge for your caregiving services. Be fair when setting your hourly, daily or weekly rate. Talk to other caregivers in your area and find out what they are charging, or do some research on the Internet. You can also ask other parents how much they have paid caregivers in the past. Your requested rate will vary according to the type of caregiving job. For example, if the parents want you to work one evening a week, you will most likely charge an hourly rate. If the family hires you to work three days per week, you may charge a daily rate. If the family hires you as a full-time caregiver, you may charge a weekly salary that also includes your meals. You may also want to vary your rate depending on the job expectations. For example, some caregivers charge more for additional children or for extra duties, such as cleaning or cooking.

BE SMART, BE SAFE! Even if you really like the family or want the money, you should never take a caregiving job that exceeds your abilities or one that you are uncomfortable with for any other reason.

Building Your Business

Parents want caregivers who take the job seriously and act professionally from start to finish. To help your caregiving business grow and thrive:

- Only accept jobs for which you have the right skills and experience.

- Treat families like customers. Show them the same respect and courtesy that you expect to be shown by them. Let them know you appreciate their business.

- Be reliable. It doesn't matter if you are the best caregiver in the world—if you are late or cancel appointments all the time, then you won't receive job offers. Only cancel a caregiving appointment if you are sick or for a family emergency. (By the way, you *should* cancel if you are sick—no one wants your germs!) If you must cancel, let the family know as far in advance as possible.

- Dress in clean, comfortable clothes that are appropriate for caregiving. Make sure your hair and hands are neat and clean, and keep your fingernails trimmed and smooth. Avoid wearing sharp jewelry that could scratch a child or dangly jewelry that a child could pull on.

- Come prepared! Pack a bag with a first aid kit, a piece of fruit or an energy bar, an extra shirt (in case of accidents) and any supplies you might need for activities you have planned to do with the kids. It's a good idea to put your *Advanced Child Care Training Handbook* in your caregiving bag too.

- Arrive at the job on time or slightly early.

- Remember that the kids are your top priority while you are caregiving. You are there to have fun with them and to keep them safe. That means your focus should be on the kids—not on your homework, your friends, your mobile device or the television—while you are "on duty."

- Use your mobile phone only to make emergency calls or to receive calls from your family or the child's parents. If you do need to make or take a call, keep the conversation brief.

- Model good behavior while you are on the job. Wash your hands before preparing or eating food, after using the bathroom, and after coughing or blowing your nose, and encourage the kids to do the same. Be careful of the language you use. Follow all of the family's instructions and house rules. (Bonus: the kids will be happier, feel more secure and behave better if you follow their usual routines!)

- If you intend to use any equipment in the house, such as the television, video gaming system, computer or kitchen appliances, ask the parents' permission first. Do not use the equipment unless you have permission, even after the kids have gone to bed.

- Don't help yourself to food or drinks unless you have been given permission.

- Clean up after yourself and the kids. Put away any toys or games that were used, and tidy up the kitchen after having a snack or a meal. In general, leave the house as you found it.

- Be mindful of the family's pets. Some families do not let their cats or dogs go outside. If you and the kids go outside, make sure to shut the door behind you so that no pets escape.

- Stay awake unless you are on an overnight job.

- Never snoop! Don't go into rooms that you don't need to be in to do your job, and do not look through drawers, cabinets or closets.

- Don't have friends over while you are caregiving.

- It goes without saying, but never smoke or use drugs or alcohol while you are caregiving!

- When the parents come home, tell them about what happened while they were away. One easy way to do this is to fill out the **Caregiver's Report Record**, which you can download from your online course. Check out a sample in Appendix B. When communicating with parents about their children, be positive and show enthusiasm for your job. If you ever have to talk to parents about an issue with their children, make sure you also mention positive things.

- Keep records that will help you stay organized and run your business efficiently. You can create a file for each family where you can store important information, such as contact information and details about the children and the care they require.

- Record notes each time you work for the family, including what you did, what you charged, and what went well and what did not.

- Ask the families you work for if they can help you to improve your caregiving skills by giving you feedback. A true professional is always open to constructive criticism and looks to improve!

2 YOU'RE THE LEADER

When you are caregiving, you are the person in charge when the parents are away. The kids will look to you for direction, and you are responsible for keeping them safe, following the house rules and making sure everyone has fun during your visit. But what happens if the kids don't listen when you tell them it is time for bed, or they can't agree on what game to play or movie to watch? How will you handle fighting or temper tantrums? As the person in charge, you need to be able to make good decisions, encourage good behavior, and respond to misbehavior appropriately if it occurs. You need to be a good leader.

Leading the Way

A leader is a person who guides and motivates others. As a caregiver, you are responsible for helping the kids to behave, keeping them safe and making sure everybody has fun. To meet these responsibilities, you must be a leader!

Be a Leader!

There are many different ways to lead. Just like you pick the right outfit to wear depending on the occasion, you will need to pick the right leadership style to use depending on the situation. As a caregiver, you will probably use all of these leadership styles at one point or another. Knowing how and when to use each leadership style will help you while you're on the job.

Hands-off!

If the kids are getting along well and no important decisions need to be made, you can use a "hands-off" leadership style. For example, if three sisters have been playing a board game without any conflicts and a slight disagreement comes up, you don't need to step in. In a case like this, you can just let the girls work things out on their own. Using the hands-off leadership style can keep you from seeming too bossy and it gives the children a chance to learn how to solve disagreements on their own. If the conflict gets worse or the children can't resolve the problem themselves, then it's time for you to step in and take action.

Let's take a vote!

When a decision needs to be made that affects everyone but doesn't involve safety, you can use a style of leadership called the democratic leadership style. For example, if the kids can't decide whether to go to the park or watch a DVD, don't immediately decide for them. Instead, ask each child to say what he or she would prefer to do and develop a plan together. Then, take a vote on the best course of action. Try to keep the discussion positive. This approach allows each child to feel like his or her opinions are listened to and respected.

You're important!

Empathy is the quality of trying to understand another person's situation, feelings or point of view. When you use an empathetic leadership style, you focus on making people feel valued and cared for. An empathetic leadership style works best in situations when it is more important to focus on how the kids feel rather than on how they are acting. If the kids are safe and not hurting each other, take your time and listen to what each child has to say and ignore any minor attention-seeking behavior. By focusing on each child's feelings and taking the time to listen to his or her concerns, you can earn the child's trust. The empathetic leadership style also works well when you are just getting to know the kids you are caregiving for, or when emotions are running high.

Try to keep the discussion positive. This approach allows each child to feel like his or her opinions are listened to and respected.

Do this, now!

Sometimes you may need to tell the kids what to do with little or no discussion (to keep someone safe or prevent injury). For example, if a child is about to pull the dog's tail, you must tell the child to stop and separate the child from the dog. You don't have time to discuss the situation because immediate action is needed. Situations like this call for a style of leadership called the directive leadership style.

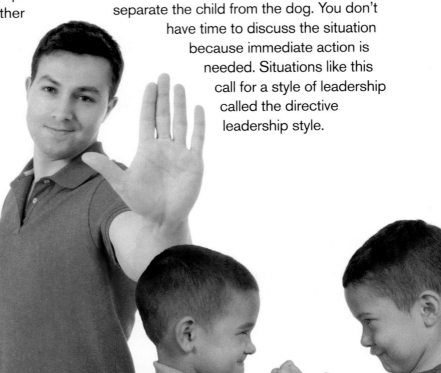

Sharpen Your Leadership Skills

Leaders use many different skills to guide and motivate others. Anyone can learn to be a leader. As with other skills, the more you practice, the better you will become. Let's take a look at some of the skills good leaders use.

Modeling good behavior

A role model sets an example for others to follow. Modeling good behavior is important because the children will look up to you and follow the example you set. Modeling is also one of the simplest ways to lead. For example, when children see you washing your hands before a meal, they will want to do the same. You can be a good role model by:

- Following the house rules and the parents' instructions.

- Showing enthusiasm, having a positive attitude and making the best out of difficult situations.

- Treating others with kindness, compassion, courtesy and respect.

- Focusing on safety.

Communicating

Being able to communicate well with others is a very important skill for leaders to have. A good communicator is able to express herself clearly in a way that the other person is able to understand. But good communication isn't all about talking! It's about listening, too. It is especially important for caregivers to know how to talk and listen to kids. Here are some valuable tips for communicating with children:

- **Keep it simple.** Use short sentences and words the child understands.

- **Keep it positive.** Tell the kids what you want them to do instead of what they shouldn't do. For example, say "Please put your plate in the sink" instead of "Don't leave your plate on the table."

- **Be specific.** Tell the kids exactly what you like or don't like about what they are doing. For example, when Lucy picks up her toys, say "I like it when you pick up your toys" rather than "You're a good girl." If William throws his blocks, say "I don't like it when you throw your blocks" rather than "You're a bad boy."

- **Explain why.** When you need to ask a child to do something (or to stop doing something), explain why. Although the reason behind your request may seem obvious to you, it's not always obvious to the child. If the child understands the reason for your request, he may be more likely to do what you are asking him to do. Also, sometimes kids have trouble understanding how their actions affect other people, so it is important to explain this to them. For example, after you ask William to stop throwing his blocks, you could explain why: "When you throw your blocks, it scares me because you might hurt yourself or somebody else."

- **Limit choices.** Give the child reasonable choices between acceptable options. This will help you to avoid having to say "no" if the child asks for something you cannot provide or that is off limits. For example, instead of asking the child "What do you want to drink?" ask "Would you like milk or water to drink?"

- **Speak calmly.** Speak in a calm voice, even if you are upset or angry. If a child is yelling or screaming, say "I can't understand you when you yell" or "You need to tell me why you are upset so that I can help."

- **Be a good listener.** Sit down or kneel so that you are at the child's eye level, and make eye contact. Ask questions to make sure you understand what the child is telling you. If you cannot do what the child wants right away, let her know you are listening and have heard the request. For example, if the child wants to go to the park but you need to check with her parents first, explain this to the child.

- **Use humor.** When things are tense, acting goofy or telling a joke can sometimes lighten the mood. Just be sure to never make fun of the child! And be aware that sometimes humor can backfire, so you need to be careful about how and when you use it.

Motivating

One very important thing that good leaders do is to help the people they are leading to be successful. When you are caregiving, you want to help the kids to stay safe, have a good time and behave well. Read on for some of the best ways you can motivate the children to help achieve these goals:

- **Give positive feedback.** Let the kids know when they are behaving well and recognize their efforts. Give positive feedback often. When someone praises our efforts, we're more likely to continue doing whatever earned us the praise, right? The same is true of kids. Positive feedback helps them feel good about themselves and makes it more likely that they will behave. If the children misbehave, then use corrective feedback to stop or change how they are acting. Corrective feedback means telling children what *to do* instead of what they did wrong.

- **Have a plan.** Come to each caregiving job prepared. Plan out activities ahead of time. Bring extra supplies and have a back-up plan ready in case things change.

- **Be flexible and creative.** You may need to adjust your plan to help keep everyone on track. As long as things are safe and you follow the household rules, then it's OK to change plans. Treat each caregiving job individually, and try not to fall into routines.

- **Set some "ground rules" for your time together, and then review these rules with the kids.** Keep your list of rules short and age-appropriate, and phrase them in a positive way. Focus on areas such as safety, good manners and following the parents' instructions. For example, you could tell the kids that the rules for your time together are: "Be nice to each other," "Stay with me at all times" and "Use indoor voices when we're in the house." Many families may already have a set of house rules that their kids are expected to follow. If this is the case, you can review these rules with the kids; there is no need to add extra rules.

- **Seek input.** When safety or other important issues are not at stake, include the children in decision making. For example, if there is a choice between playtime activities, ask the kids what they want to do. (In other words, use the democratic leadership style!) Of course, you need to make the important decisions, such as those involving safety.

Taking action

People look to leaders to take action when no one else will. In difficult situations it is easy to think that someone else will handle things or that solving the problem is not your responsibility. But if no one takes responsibility, then no one will act. A leader will risk sounding foolish or standing out to make the right choice in a difficult situation. There are three steps to taking action:

1. **Notice that action is needed**. Be alert for changes that could signal a problem. For example, maybe you notice that the kids have started playing too aggressively. Or maybe you are out in the backyard, and the sky is getting dark and you hear thunder.

2. **Take responsibility.** Ask yourself if action is needed and then take responsibility for the situation. For example, recognize that the roughhousing could result in injury to one of the kids, or that a storm is coming and that it is your responsibility to keep the kids safe.

3. **Act.** Don't worry about looking foolish or standing out. Take action to fix the situation. For example, ask the roughhousing kids to calm down a little or try to get them interested in another activity. In the case of the coming thunderstorm, tell the kids it is time to move inside. Remember, only do what you are trained to do and what you can do safely.

Decision making

When you are in charge, you might have to decide how to handle a challenging situation on your own. Parents rely on you to make good decisions. When you are faced with a tough situation, use the FIND decision-making model to help you decide what to do:

- **F**igure out the problem. Focus on the exact problem that is causing trouble.

- **I**dentify possible solutions. Think about all the possible ways you could solve the problem.

- **N**ame pros and cons for each solution. Think about the positive outcomes that could occur with each possible solution that you identified. Also think about possible negative outcomes.

- **D**ecide which solution is best, then act on it.

Child Abuse and Neglect

Child abuse is the term for hurting a child physically, emotionally or sexually. Child neglect is the failure to provide for the child's basic needs. If you suspect that a child is abused or neglected, speak with someone you trust about your concerns. You can also call the Childhelp National Child Abuse Hotline at 1-800-4-A-CHILD (1-800-422-4453) for advice and help. You should call the police if you feel that the situation is life threatening.

Some signs that might indicate that child abuse or neglect is occurring include:

- Unexplained bruises, burns or scars, especially if the child has multiple injuries in various stages of healing, or if the injuries have recognizable shapes (like round burns caused by the end of a cigarette or a bruise in the shape of a belt buckle).

- A child who dislikes physical contact, such as hugging or being held.

- A child who seems fearful, anxious or withdrawn, especially in the presence of adults.

- A child who cries a lot or seems very sad.

- A child who is very aggressive or tries to hurt himself or others.

- A child who is afraid of undressing.

- Unclean or unsafe living conditions.

- Inadequate clothing, a lack of personal cleanliness (for example, unwashed clothing, skin and hair; unbrushed teeth), or signs of not having enough to eat or drink.

What to Do When Children Misbehave

Even when you're doing your best to be a great leader, sometimes your followers don't always cooperate. Dealing with difficult behaviors is one of the most common caregiving challenges because, at some point, all kids misbehave. Kids often need help learning how to control their behavior and how to express themselves. As a caregiver, your responsibilities include trying to prevent misbehavior and dealing with it appropriately when it occurs.

Young children learn how to act and behave by testing boundaries, asserting their independence, and observing adults and older children. When the children behave inappropriately, it is your job to guide them to understand how to behave more appropriately. Kids misbehave for many reasons. Some of the most common reasons are that the child is:

- Tired, frustrated, hungry or scared.

- In need of attention.

- Bored.

- Feeling jealous of, or competitive toward, a brother or sister.

- Testing limits.

- Asserting her independence.

- Repeating behavior he has been rewarded for in the past.

- Copying someone else's bad behavior.

REMEMBER!
Children are allowed to express their feelings, even angry ones, but it is not OK for children to behave badly when they are angry. Strong emotions are no excuse for bad behavior.

A+ Behavior

There are lots of things you can do to help the kids you are caregiving behave well while you are together. Read on for some tips!

- **Let the kids know when they are behaving well.** Children respond well to praise.

- **Let the kids know the "rules" when you first arrive on the job.** Remember to keep your list of rules short and age-appropriate, and phrase them in a positive manner.

- **Follow the normal household routines as closely as possible.** For example, serve dinner at the usual time, have children do their regular chores and allow them to play video games after doing their homework if that is what they typically do.

- **Give the children advance notice of approaching changes.** Transitions are difficult for many kids (especially for younger children). This is especially true if they involve something the child doesn't want to do. For example, if bedtime is coming up, say "Bedtime is in 15 minutes."

- **Have a plan for having fun. Plan a few activities to do with kids.** Try to include activities that will allow them to burn off some energy, as well as quieter activities. But remember to be flexible. The kids might have other ideas about what they would like to do.

- **Stay positive and enthusiastic.** Children will follow your example.

- **Keep off-limit items out of sight.** Out of sight, out of mind!

- **Be fair; don't play favorites.** Try to make each child in your care feel equally appreciated and valued.

- **Whenever possible, give children choices.** Letting kids choose between acceptable options helps them to feel like they have some control over their own lives.

Correcting Bad Behavior

When a child misbehaves, make sure the child knows that you are unhappy with what he *did* rather than with *him*. Children need to know that you won't stop liking them if they misbehave. When you respond to misbehavior, give corrective feedback and use positive and respectful requests to stop or change the behavior.

When a child misbehaves, you have three choices of how you can respond: do nothing, say something or physically do something. Each of these methods works best in different situations.

- **Do nothing.** This means that you ignore the child's misbehavior if it is safe to do so. Doing nothing works well when a child is misbehaving to get your attention. For example, if a child throws a temper tantrum but is not hurting himself or anyone else, you can ignore the behavior.

- **Say something.** This means you tell the child what to do or what not to do. Saying something is the method you will use to solve most common caregiving problems.

  ○ Stay calm and use a neutral tone even if the child is screaming. Yelling back will only make things worse.

  ○ Explain to the child why her behavior is unacceptable.

REMEMBER!
Never shake, slap, hit or spank a child! You should also never shout at, criticize or make fun of a child; lock a child up; or punish a child by not allowing him to eat or drink, rest or use the bathroom.

○ Offer an acceptable alternative. If the child really wants to play a video game but it's not allowed, offer to play a card game instead.

○ Use "when…then" statements. For example, "When you put on your shoes, then we can go to the park."

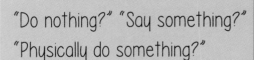

"Do nothing?" "Say something?" "Physically do something?"

ADHD

Attention deficit hyperactivity disorder (ADHD) is a condition that a doctor may diagnose when a child has an especially hard time paying attention or controlling his behavior. Children with ADHD often lose interest in whatever they are doing quickly. They may have a hard time sitting still or waiting their turn, and they may interrupt others when they are talking. They often act impulsively, which means they do things without thinking about the consequences. Kids who have ADHD are usually diagnosed with it in preschool, and boys are more likely to have ADHD than girls. If you care for a child with ADHD, the parents will likely have special instructions that you should follow.

■ **Physically do something.** This means that you take physical action to stop the child from misbehaving. You will use this method when the child is in danger of hurting herself or someone else. For example, if the child is about to throw a toy, then take the toy away. Or, if a child tries to hit you, gently, but firmly, grasp her arm before she can hit you and say, "I won't let you hit me. If you're angry, tell me with words." Sometimes, just moving the child to another location creates a distraction and is enough to stop the bad behavior.

Understanding Kids of All Ages: Helping Kids to Follow the Rules

Infant (Newborn to 12 months) 	■ Infants are completely dependent and have no ability to understand, follow or break rules. ■ Infants cry because this is the only way they are able to tell you that they need something.
Toddler (1 to 3 years old) 	■ Toddlers have a strong desire for independence and often have trouble following rules. ■ Toddlers need to test limits, which means they will often say "no" when asked to do something. ■ Temper tantrums are normal and the toddler's way of expressing frustration. ■ Toddlers may also hit, bite or kick others out of frustration, because they lack the ability to fully express their feelings with words.
Preschooler (3 to 4 years old) 	■ Preschoolers are beginning to know the difference between right and wrong behavior, so they are better able to follow rules. ■ Preschoolers enjoy being involved in making up the rules. ■ Preschoolers may become frustrated when there are too many rules or the rules are too confusing. Focus on a few simple well-chosen rules instead. ■ Preschoolers may make mistakes and not follow the rules. Gently remind the preschooler of the rule and why it is important to follow it. ■ Preschoolers are developing the vocabulary to express their feelings, leading to a decrease in behaviors such as temper tantrums, biting, kicking and hitting.
Younger School-Age Child (5 to 7 years old) 	■ Younger school-age children are beginning to develop reasoning skills and the ability to understand "cause and effect," so they are better able to understand why rules exist and why following them is important. ■ Younger school-age children often "aim to please" by demonstrating their knowledge of, and ability to follow, the rules. Praising good behavior works especially well with this age group! ■ Younger school-age children also enjoy being involved in setting the rules.
Older School-Age Child (8 to 10 years old)	■ Older school-age children understand the difference between right and wrong. ■ Older school-age children have an increased ability to understand and accept consequences. ■ Older school-age children may go back and forth from being cooperative to being difficult to motivate.

Using Consequences

Promoting positive behavior and taking action when the kids misbehave will help you handle most situations. But sometimes you will need to use consequences to help make sure kids follow rules. Be sure to find out from the parents before they leave what consequences you should use if a child misbehaves. In some cases, you may have to come up with a consequence to help you enforce rules.

Consequences should generally be used in the following order:

- **Natural consequences.** Natural consequences are the natural results of an action. For example, you give a child a cookie and ask him to sit at the table to eat it. You tell the child, "Please sit at the table to eat your cookie. If you get up and walk around, the cookie could drop on the floor and then Sparky will gobble it up! If Sparky eats your cookie, I can't give you another one." If the child leaves the table and the cookie falls on the floor, the *natural* consequence is that the dog eats the cookie and the child is not given another cookie to replace the one that fell. Use natural consequences if they are safe, and make sure children know them ahead of time.

- **Logical consequences.** Logical consequences are those that are closely related to an action. An example of a logical consequence would be asking an older child who knocks over a younger child's blocks to help restack them. Logical consequences only work if they seem to go with the misbehavior.

- **Withholding privileges.** Withholding privileges works best with school-age children and preschoolers. If a child does not follow a rule that has been explained to him, do not allow him to do something he enjoys, such as watching television or playing video games.

- **Time-out.** A time-out is a consequence that involves removing the child from the situation and putting her in a quiet place for a brief amount of time. This technique works well for older toddlers and over-excited preschoolers, but avoid using it too much. Give no more than 1 minute of time-out for each year of age. For example, a 4-year-old would stay in time-out for no more than 4 minutes. Put the child in a safe spot where there are no distractions, and make sure you can see the child at all times.

Common Challenging Behaviors

Common challenging behaviors include temper tantrums; biting, hitting and kicking; and fighting.

Temper tantrums

A temper tantrum is a strong outburst of challenging behavior, such as whining, crying, screaming, kicking, hitting or breath-holding. Toddlers and preschoolers often have temper tantrums when they are told "no" or when they want to do something on their own but can't. Kids this age don't always know how to use words to express feelings like anger or frustration. Temper tantrums are their way of expressing these feelings. A child who is tired, hungry or over-excited, or who is trying to get your attention, may also throw a temper tantrum.

Breath-Holding Spells

Some children may momentarily stop breathing when they are upset, startled or hurt. These episodes are called "breath-holding spells," and in children who have them, they often occur during a temper tantrum or when the child is crying. The child has no control over the breath-holding spells—she cannot deliberately bring one on, nor can she stop one from happening. Most children who have breath-holding spells outgrow them between the ages of 4 and 8 years.

A breath-holding spell can be very scary to see. A crying child may gasp and appear to stop breathing. The child's face may turn deep blue or very pale, her eyes may roll back in her head, and usually she will pass out. Sometimes the child will twitch and jerk during a breath-holding spell. Within a minute, the child starts breathing again and the spell passes.

If a child is known to have breath-holding spells, the parents will probably let you know this in advance. If you suspect that a child is having a breath-holding spell, help the child lie down on the floor. That way, if she loses consciousness, she won't fall and hurt herself. If you have a washcloth nearby, wet it and place it on the child's forehead until she starts breathing. The child should start breathing again within 1 minute; if she does not, then the child is experiencing something other than a breath-holding spell and you will need to give appropriate emergency care according to your level of training. Do not put anything in the child's mouth. After the spell, comfort the child, and be sure to let the parents know what happened when they return.

Minimizing a child's feelings of frustration may help to prevent a temper tantrum. Let the child choose between limited options whenever possible, and keep off-limit items out of sight. Stick to normal routines. During playtime, keep toys that may cause frustration out of sight. Make sure toys are age-appropriate, and that there are enough toys for everyone. If you see that a child is starting to get frustrated or angry, help her to use words to express herself. For example, teach the child to say "Please give my toy back" if another child tries to take her toy away.

Making sure the child's needs are met may also help to prevent a tantrum from occurring. Give the child plenty of positive attention. Prevent the child from becoming too wound up by following high-energy activities with quieter ones. Offer drinks and snacks regularly, and stick to normal naptimes and bedtimes.

If you see that a child is gearing up to have a temper tantrum, help the child to take a break from the situation. For example, try another activity or change

How Old Is Too Old?

Although school-age children (5 years and older) may stomp or slam a door in anger, they are too old for temper tantrums. If a school-age child is having a temper tantrum, give him some time to gain control and then try to find out why he felt that behavior was necessary. School-age children are also old enough to understand that biting, hitting and kicking are wrong and that these behaviors hurt other people. However, sometimes older children still misbehave in this manner, especially with their brothers or sisters. If a school-age child has a temper tantrum or bites, kicks or hits someone else, make a note in your Caregiver's Report, and be sure to let the parents know about the behavior when they return.

locations. This may be enough to stop the tantrum in its tracks. But if a child does have a temper tantrum:

- Don't yell or scream. Keep your cool— kids can learn from your example.

- Ignore the temper tantrum when possible. If the child isn't hurting herself or others or being destructive, you can let the temper tantrum run its course.

- After the temper tantrum is over, encourage the child to put her feelings into words. Listen to her, and try to understand what is upsetting her. Give the child a hug and praise her for calming down and getting control of her feelings. But remember, if the meltdown occurred because the child wanted something you didn't give her, don't give it to her now. This just rewards the bad behavior! Instead, allow the child to make a choice between two acceptable solutions.

Biting, hitting and kicking

Biting, hitting and kicking are common behaviors for toddlers and young preschoolers. At this age, children may not know that these behaviors are wrong and can hurt someone. Children may bite, hit or kick for many of the same reasons they may have a temper tantrum (for example, to express anger or frustration, to get your attention, or because they are tired, hungry or over-excited).

Many of the same strategies you can use to prevent temper tantrums can also prevent behaviors such as biting, hitting and kicking. If a child does bite, hit or kick, don't overreact. Instead:

- Comfort the child who was hurt before you deal with the child who did the hurting.

- Encourage the child to explain the problem in her own words.

- Explain appropriate behavior. For example, say "It's not OK to hit people when you're mad. If you're mad because your brother took your toy, politely ask him if you can have it back."

- Ask questions that will help the child understand how the person she hurt feels. For example, say "Has anyone ever bitten you?" (Although it may seem logical to bite the child to show her how it feels to be bitten, don't ever do this! This just models inappropriate behavior and will confuse the child.)

- Help the child to take a break from the situation. Change activities or locations. Suggest a nap if the child seems tired, or a snack or drink if she seems hungry or thirsty.

- If the child continues this behavior, then a consequence such as withholding a privilege or using a time-out may be necessary.

Sibling rivalry

Sibling rivalry is the jealousy, competition and fighting that breaks out between brothers or sisters (siblings) over everything from toys to attention. It is not unusual for siblings to swing back and forth from fighting to getting along well with each other. There are many causes for sibling rivalry:

- A child who is trying to establish her individuality may compete with a sibling.

- A child who feels he is getting less attention than a sibling may act out.

- A child may pick a fight with a sibling just so the sibling will pay attention to him or her.

Sibling rivalry does have a positive side. Working things out with their brothers and sisters gives kids a chance to develop important skills like getting along with others and being able to see another person's point of view. Nevertheless, while you are in charge, you will probably prefer to avoid having to deal with sibling rivalry! You can help prevent fights among brothers and sisters from breaking out by being sure to give everyone one-on-one attention. Never play favorites or compare one child to another. Plan activities that are fun for everyone and that encourage cooperation rather than competition.

If a fight does break out, try not to get involved unless someone is in danger of getting hurt. If you have to step in, solve the problem *with* the siblings, not *for* them. Follow these tips:

- Don't yell or lecture.

- Don't put too much focus on figuring out which child is to blame.

- Separate the kids until they're calm. (If the kids are really upset, you might have to move each of them to a different room to get them to calm down. If so, make sure you choose rooms where you can keep an eye on both kids.) When the kids calm down, encourage them to talk things out.

- Encourage win-win negotiations, where each side gains something.

- Remember that not everything has to be fair and equal. For example, an older child may be allowed to play with a certain toy that a younger child is not.

3 SAFETY ON THE JOB

As a caregiver, your most important responsibility is to keep the kids, and yourself, safe. Of course, sometimes accidents will happen—that's why they're called "accidents." And some situations that arise, such as weather events, are completely out of your control. But you can help prevent many accidents and injuries, and keep everyone safe, by being prepared, knowledgeable and alert while you are on the job.

Staying Safe at Home

While you are in the family's home, it's important to take steps to make sure the home stays secure. In general, it's never a good idea to let strangers know that you are in a house alone with kids. Potential criminals who have this information will see the house as an easy target for a break-in or other crime. It's also important to use security features, like door locks, to keep strangers out and yourself and the kids safely inside.

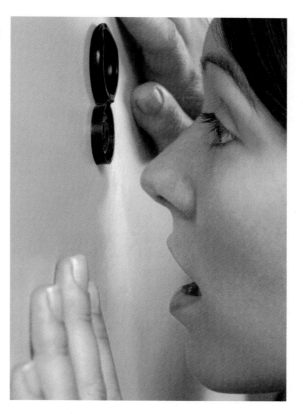

If the family has a home electronic security system, ask the parents if they would like you to use it, and have them show you how to turn it on and off. Always use the "low-tech" home security system (that is, locks on doors and windows) too. After the parents leave, be sure to lock the door behind them, and make sure the windows are locked. If you are caregiving in the evening, turn on the outside lights when it starts to get dark. If you hear an unusual noise, don't go outside to check it out. Instead, call the child's parents, a family member or friend or the police if you are worried about it.

If someone knocks at the door, look out through a peephole or window to see who is there. Never open the door to anyone except the child's parents, your own family member or professional responders who you have called to the house because of an emergency. Even if the person on the doorstep seems to have a valid reason for being there (for example, a delivery person who is delivering a package, a service technician who is there to repair something inside the house or a neighbor who wants to return a borrowed item), do not let the person in the house. The person can come back another time, when the parents are home.

Talk to the parents before they leave about whether or not they want you to answer the house phone while they are away. If an answering machine is available, most parents will probably prefer that you just let the machine pick up. If they do want you to answer their phone, never tell callers that you are the caregiver or that the parents aren't home. Instead, say the person the caller wants to speak to is "busy" and ask to take a message. Be prepared with a pen and paper so you can write down the name of the caller and a number where the caller can be reached. If you get a phone call that scares you, call the child's parents or the police.

Just as you shouldn't tell people at the door or on the phone that you are caregiving, you shouldn't post anything on social media that will let others know that you are caregiving. The only people who need to know that you are alone in a house with children are the parents who hired you. When you tag photos, update your status or "check in," you give everyone on the Internet a lot of information about where you are and what you are doing. If this information gets into the wrong hands, it could be just as dangerous as letting a stranger into the home!

It's not likely that an intruder will break into the home while you are caregiving, especially if you take precautions to keep the home secure. But in the unlikely event of a home break-in, remember that your job is to protect yourself and the kids, not household belongings! If you can see a way to get yourself and the kids out of the house without the intruder noticing, do it. Otherwise, try to remain undetected and wait for the intruder to leave.

BE SMART, BE SAFE! Never leave the house without the children, even for a short period of time—not even to bring a pet back into the house or to get a toy from the driveway. What if the door locks behind you and you can't get back in, or one of the kids gets into something dangerous during the brief time that you were outside? Be safe and take the kids with you wherever you go.

Staying Safe While You Are Out and About

When you are caregiving, you may spend most of your time inside the house or playing with the kids in the yard. Some parents may not want you to take the kids on outings. Therefore, if you are thinking about taking the kids somewhere (for example, to a nearby park or playground, or to get ice cream at the shop down the street), be sure to clear this plan with the parents before they leave. Again, they may prefer that you and the kids just hang out at home and/or play in the yard while they are away.

If the parents tell you it is OK to take the kids outside to play or on outings, take steps to protect them from sunburn, insect bites and other injuries before leaving the house. Find out from the parents if they want you to use sunscreen and insect repellant on the kids. If they do, apply these products before you leave the house. Make sure the children are dressed appropriately for whatever

activity you have planned. For example, the drawstring of a hooded sweatshirt, a scarf or a necklace can get caught on playground equipment, so these are not good choices if you are planning to go to the playground. Make sure children always wear shoes when playing outside.

Staying Safe in the Yard

If you will be with the kids in the backyard, make sure the front door remains locked.

When you are outside with the kids, keep them close by so that you can see and hear them at all times. Take a quick look around the yard for anything that could pose hazards to the kids, such as sharp garden tools, ladders, a water-filled bucket or garbage can, or shrubs with branches or thorns that could scratch. Remove the hazard, or keep kids out of the part of the yard where the hazard is located. Make sure the

kids stay in the yard and out of the street. Don't let kids play near parked cars, on or near the curb, or near storm drains. (Storm drains are especially dangerous after it has rained.) To lower the risk of tick or spider bites, don't let the kids play near woodpiles, in wooded or brushy areas, or in areas with tall grass. Be especially cautious if the family has a pool. Even a wading pool poses a drowning risk. (See the section, Preventing Drowning.)

Safe Fun in the Sun

Being outside is good for kids. It gives them a chance to run and jump and just enjoy some fresh air and sunshine. But too much sun exposure can lead to a painful sunburn and raises the risk for serious health problems in the future, like skin cancer. To help keep kids (and yourself!) safe in the sun:

- Notice the time of day before going outside. The sun's rays are strongest between 10 a.m. and 4 p.m. During these hours, avoid exposure to the sun or seek shade, if possible.

- Know that water, sand and snow reflect the sun's rays, increasing exposure and the risk for sunburn.

- Have the kids wear protective clothing, like a hat and sunglasses, whenever possible. If the weather is not too hot, long-sleeved shirts and pants can offer some protection from the sun too.

- Find out from the parents which sunscreen product, if any, they would like you to use on their children. Some children might have allergies or sensitivities to certain sunscreens or all sunscreens.

- Apply sunscreen to the kids (and to yourself) 30 minutes before you go outside, even if it is cloudy out. (It is still possible to burn on a cloudy day.) Reapply every 2 hours and after swimming, exercising or sweating.

- Be aware that sunscreen is not recommended for babies younger than 6 months. If a baby younger than 6 months is outside, it's best to protect the baby from the sun by making sure she is dressed in adequate clothing and by keeping her in the shade (for example, underneath an umbrella or the canopy of a stroller). If the parents do want you to apply sunscreen to a baby younger than 6 months, apply only a small amount to the baby's face and the back of her hands.

Sun safety isn't just important for kids. It's important for you, too. When you are choosing a sunscreen for yourself, choose one labeled "broad-spectrum" with a sun protection factor (SPF) of at least 15; an SPF of 30 or higher is even better. Apply sunscreen every day, even if you aren't going to be outside for long. The sun's rays can also damage your skin through the windows of a car or building! Embrace your natural skin color—avoid "laying out" in the sun to tan or going to tanning beds. And don't think that if you have naturally dark skin, you are safe from sun damage. Darker-skinned people need to take the same precautions as lighter-skinned people to protect themselves from too much sun exposure!

Staying Safe in the Great Outdoors

When you are outside with kids, keep an eye out for things that could hurt them:

- **Tripping hazards:** uneven ground, roots that stick up, toys or tools left in the yard

- **Drowning hazards:** any container that has water in it, even just a small amount, is a potential drowning hazard!

- **Plants that can cause rashes or poisoning:** watch out for plants with "leaves of three," which can often cause rashes, and plants with pretty berries, which kids are often tempted to put in their mouths!

- **Plants with thorns or branches that could cause scratches**

- **Objects that could cause cuts or puncture wounds:** sharp tools, trash (such as broken glass or open aluminum cans), nails

- **Animals and animal droppings**

- **Insects and spiders**

Staying Safe When You Are Away from the House

Before leaving the house with the children, tell the child's parents where you are going, your planned route, when you are leaving and when you will be back. Pack a bag to take with you that includes the house key, your first aid kit, your mobile phone or change for a pay phone, the phone number where the parents can be reached and anything you need for the kids (such as sunscreen and insect repellant). Use the bathroom and make sure the kids do the same. Lock the door when you leave the house and make sure all the windows are closed and locked.

While you are walking, hold the hands of young children. Position the children so that they are between you and the houses, not between you and the street.

Only cross streets at the crosswalk, and always look left, then right, then left again before crossing.

You should make sure everyone is supervised and safe. This can be challenging, especially if you and the kids are of opposite genders. Check with the parents ahead of time to learn how they would like you to handle this tricky situation. If there is anyone in the restroom who makes you uncomfortable for any reason, take the kids and leave.

Being aware of your surroundings and what is going on around you is key to staying safe. You should never stay in a situation where you feel threatened or uncomfortable. For example, if you are out and a stranger keeps trying to talk to you, ignore the person and take the kids somewhere safe. Similarly, if you feel like someone is following you, walk

Rural Safety

If you live in a rural community, some of the families you work for may own farms or ranches, or just large pieces of undeveloped land. When this is the case, make sure you ask the parents where the children are allowed to be on the property and which areas are not safe for them. For example, there may be buildings (such as barns or silos) or other areas on the property (such as fields where animals are kept) that are off limits to the children. It's a good idea to ask the parents to take you on a walk around the property to note the possible hazards. These can include:

- Bodies of water, such as ponds or lakes
- Farm equipment and machinery
- Farm animals
- Electric fences

Children who live on farms or ranches may have chores they need to complete while you are watching them. Make sure to ask the parents what the children are allowed to do, and supervise them at all times.

In rural areas, remember that the response time for emergency medical services (EMS) personnel is longer and that the nearest neighbor may be far away.

Powers of Observation

One of the best strategies you can use to keep yourself and the kids safe while you are caregiving is to pay attention to what is going on around you. Your eyes, ears, nose and even your "gut" can alert you to potentially dangerous situations, allowing you to take quick action to keep yourself and others safe. Pay attention to:

- **What you see.** Look around and take note of what you see. Unusual sights (like a funnel cloud, flames, lightning or a wild animal that is acting strangely) are signs that you need to get somewhere safe.

- **What you hear.** Pay attention to what you are hearing. Know that when kids are involved, hearing nothing at all can be a cause for worry! Also pay attention to unusual sounds that might signal danger.

- **What you smell.** Unusual smells, like the smell of smoke, gas or chemicals, can be an early clue that something is wrong.

- **What you feel.** Some people call it a "sixth sense"—a feeling in your gut that something just isn't right. If something just doesn't seem right and you're worried, take action (such as leaving the area or calling for help).

to a police or fire station, or to a place where there are lots of other people around, like a store or restaurant.

When you get back from your outing, call or text the child's parents to let them know that you are back safely. If you get back to the house and anything looks unusual (for example, an open door, a broken window, a strange car parked outside), do not go into the house. Take the children to a safe place (such as a neighbor's house or a local business) and call 9-1-1 or the local emergency number.

BE SMART, BE SAFE! Be wary of people that you do not know who ask you for help or directions. Just say, "I'm sorry, we can't help you" and take the kids somewhere safe. It may seem rude not to help, but it's better to be safe than to be polite.

Staying Safe If You Hear Gunfire

If you and the kids are in a public building like a mall and you hear something that sounds like gunfire, get out of the building if you safely can. If you don't think you can get yourself and the children out of the building safely, then you need to take cover. You have probably practiced lockdown drills, or what to do if there is a shooter in a building. The same ideas apply here. Find a hiding place, lock or block doors, silence your mobile phone and try to avoid attracting any attention. Wait for the police to arrive.

If you are outside and you hear gunfire, everyone should lie down on the ground. Cover your head with your hands and have the children do the same. Wait for 20 to 30 minutes before leaving cover. Call 9-1-1 or the local emergency number as soon as you possibly can.

Staying Safe While Driving

If you have a valid driver's license, you may be asked to drive children to and from school, to afterschool sports or activities, or to play dates or outings as part of the caregiving job. Driving with children in the car is a big responsibility and requires a high level of knowledge and skill.

Parents will verify that you are a safe, licensed driver. They may ask to see your driver's license, proof of insurance and driving record to make sure that you are a responsible, safe driver. Some parents may even pay for you to take a defensive driving course.

If you will be using your own car to drive the kids, the parents may ask to check the safety features of your car,

properly install appropriate car seats for their children and teach you how to properly secure the child or children in the seats. The National Highway Traffic Safety Administration provides car seat recommendations for children from infants to 12 years:

- Birth to 12 Months: Rear-facing car seat.

- 1 to 3 Years: Rear-facing car seat until height/weight limit is reached and then forward-facing car seat with a harness.

- 4 to 7 Years: Forward-facing car seat with a harness until height/weight limit is reached and then booster seat.

- 8 to 12 Years: Booster seat until seat belt fits properly.

BE SMART, BE SAFE! Children 12 years old and younger should ALWAYS ride in the back seat.

Avoiding distractions while driving is essential, particularly when driving children. Using a hand-held device while driving is by far the most dangerous distracted driving activity. *Never text or call while driving!* Some parents may install a safety unit that disables electronic mobile devices every time the car is in motion to ensure that the caregiver does not text or use a hand-held device while driving.

Other activities that can distract you while you are driving include:

- Eating or drinking.

- Putting on makeup or brushing your hair.

- Talking excitedly to a passenger.

- Programming the navigation system or reading maps.

- Watching a video.

- Adjusting the radio, CD player or MP3 player.

Another potential hazard to a child while driving is accidental heat stroke caused by leaving the child unattended in a vehicle. If a child is sleeping peacefully in a car, you may forget that she is there. Or, you may be tempted to run into a store to get something without taking the child with you, telling yourself, "I hate to wake him; I will only be a second."

Prevent heatstroke-related injuries and deaths by *never* leaving a baby or child

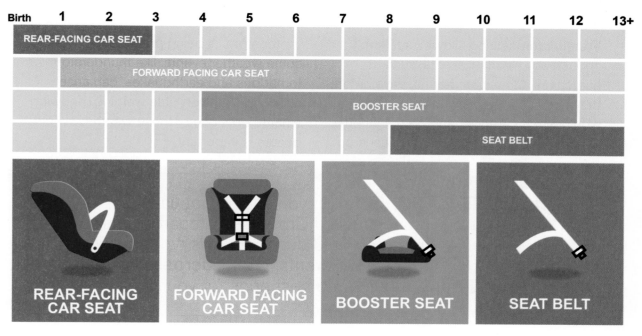

alone in a car! Also, be sure to keep the car doors and trunk of your car locked when you're not in it to keep kids from playing in a hot, parked car.

It is also helpful to create reminders and habits that establish a safety net. Put an object (such as a cell phone or purse), which you will need at your final destination, in the back of the car next to the child. Another idea is to text or call the child's parents to let them know where their child is when you drop off the child at a daycare, school or activity. You can also set an alarm on your phone as a reminder to drop off or pick up the child from daycare, school or another activity. Creating reminders and habits is especially important for caregivers because you may not be following a normal routine.

If you ever see a baby or child alone in a car, it is important to call 9-1-1 or the local emergency number right away and follow any instructions emergency personnel give you. By calling 9-1-1, you could save the life of a child!

Staying Safe During a Weather Event

Weather forecasting allows us to know about many weather events, such as hurricanes and winter storms, days before they occur. It is unlikely that parents would hire a caregiver and go out when a serious weather event like a hurricane or winter storm is being predicted. However, some weather events, like thunderstorms, tornadoes and earthquakes, can arise suddenly, with very little warning. Knowing what to do if one of these weather events occurs is important.

BE SMART, BE SAFE! Although you should not use apps while working, American Red Cross free preparedness apps will alert you right before and during various types of severe weather or other natural events. Visit **redcross.org/ prepare/mobile-apps** to find the best apps for your area.

Be Red Cross Ready!

It's important to prepare for weather events and disasters. There are three actions everyone can take that can help make a difference:

■ **Get a kit.** Every family should have an easy-to-carry emergency preparedness kit that can be used at home or taken along in case there is a need to evacuate (that is, leave the home and go to a shelter). The kit should contain first aid supplies, food and water, medications, equipment that is useful in an emergency (such as flashlights, batteries and a battery-operated radio) and copies of important documents (such as birth certificates). When you meet with the family before taking a caregiving job, ask the parents to show you where they keep their emergency preparedness kit.

■ **Make a plan.** A disaster preparedness plan maps out details like where family members should meet if they are not together when a disaster occurs, and where they will go if they need to evacuate. When you meet with the family before taking a caregiving job, ask them whether they have a disaster preparedness plan in place, and if they do, ask if they will share it with you. If you have to take the children to a shelter, let the parents know where you are going, if possible, and try to contact them when you get there.

■ **Be informed.** Know what types of weather events and disasters may occur in your area, and what actions you should take to keep yourself and others safe should a disaster or emergency occur. Know how the community alerts residents to weather events and other emergencies. For example, some communities have sirens that sound, or an automated phone call or text alert system. Have a battery-operated radio or television set available so that you can stay informed during a weather event or disaster.

You can learn more about how to help your own family be Red Cross Ready by visiting the American Red Cross website at **www.redcross.org/prepare/location/home-family**.

Thunderstorms

Thunderstorms happen year-round, but they are most common during the spring and summer months. Thunderstorms produce thunder, lighting, rain and often gusty winds. Sometimes there may even be hail.

The lightning that accompanies thunderstorms can be dangerous, especially if you are outside. If you hear thunder or see the sky start to darken, it is time to go inside, even if there is no rain. Remember, "If thunder roars, go indoors!" If you are outside and cannot reach a safe building, look for a low area. Avoid high ground; tall trees that stand alone; bodies of water; and structures such as sheds, dugouts, bleachers and picnic pavilions. These areas are not safe in a thunderstorm.

If you are driving, try to safely exit the roadway and park. Stay in the vehicle and turn on the emergency flashers until the heavy rain ends. Avoid touching metal or other surfaces that conduct electricity in and outside the vehicle.

Once you are safely inside, stay off the phone, don't turn on electrical appliances (such as the television or computer) and avoid running the water. Stay back from windows. If the power goes out, use flashlights, not candles. Many kids are afraid of thunder, lightning or both, so be prepared to comfort and reassure them. Snuggling together to read a book, playing a card or board game or singing songs may help to distract them from the scary stuff that is going on outside!

DID YOU KNOW?

If you can hear thunder, you are close enough to the storm to be in danger from lightning. Often, thunder and lightning come before the rain. Many people who have been struck by lightning report that it was not even raining when they were hit!

Tornadoes

A tornado is a spinning, funnel-shaped windstorm that moves along the ground. Tornadoes are most common in the Plains States, but they can occur in any state. When weather conditions are favorable for producing tornadoes, the National Weather Service issues a tornado *watch* for the area. When a tornado has actually been sighted in the area, a tornado *warning* is in effect. Always take tornado watches and warnings seriously!

Signs of a tornado include dark or greenish clouds, funnel-shaped clouds, blowing debris and a roaring noise, similar to the sound of a freight train. Do not wait until you actually see a tornado to seek shelter! If you see one of these signs, or a tornado watch or warning is in effect, immediately get yourself and the kids to a safe place. The safest place to be when a tornado occurs is in an underground storm shelter or basement. If you are in a house without an underground storm shelter or basement, go to the lowest level of the house and take shelter in an interior room (that is, one toward the middle of the house, without any windows) or in a hallway. Mobile homes are not safe during tornadoes. If you are in a mobile home, you need to move to an underground storm shelter or the nearest sturdy building immediately. If you work for a family that lives in a mobile home, make sure to find out from the parents where you are supposed to take the children in the event of a tornado.

Earthquakes

An earthquake occurs when the plates that make up the Earth's surface move against each other, causing the ground to move. This activity in the Earth may cause buildings to shake, windows to shatter and objects to shift or fall. The shaking can also cause fires to start and create large ocean waves (called tsunamis). Earthquakes can occur in most states, and they may occur at any time without warning.

If you are inside when an earthquake occurs, stay inside and protect yourself and the kids from falling or shifting objects by taking cover under a large, heavy object (such as a desk or table) and holding on. Remember, "Drop, cover and hold on!" If there is not a sturdy piece of furniture to take cover under, sit on the floor next to an interior wall. Cover your head and neck with your arms, and have the kids do the same. If you are outside when an earthquake occurs, stay outside but move away from buildings, trees and overhead wires.

After the main earthquake is over, use caution when opening closets or cabinets because the items inside may have shifted and could fall on you when you open the door. Avoid lighting candles or using electrical appliances because the earthquake may have caused gas leaks that could cause an explosion. Be aware that there may be aftershocks (smaller quakes that occur after the first tremor). If you feel an aftershock, drop, cover and hold on.

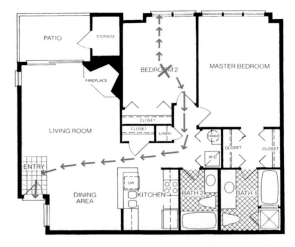

Staying Safe from House Fires

A house fire can be devastating. As a caregiver, you must know how to prevent a fire from occurring and what to do if a fire does occur.

Being Prepared for Fires

Whenever you meet with a family before taking a caregiving job, take a few minutes to get information that will help you in case there is a house fire. Many families will have a family fire escape plan in place that includes information about how to get out of the house and where family members should meet outside. Ask the parents if they will review the escape plan with you. Also ask them to show you where they keep equipment used in a fire emergency, like escape ladders and fire extinguishers. If you are caregiving for a family who lives in a high-rise apartment building, make sure you know where fire stairs and exits are located, and how to open any security bars or doors. Ask the parents to test both the smoke alarms and carbon monoxide (CO) detectors with you so that you will know the sound of the alarms in case they go off.

Oh No, CO!

Carbon monoxide (CO) is a gas that is produced whenever fossil fuels (such as gas, coal or oil) are burned. CO can also be produced during a house fire.

When equipment that burns fossil fuels is ventilated properly, CO is not a problem. But if the equipment or ventilation system is faulty, or if equipment that is only supposed to be run outdoors is run inside in an enclosed area, toxic levels of CO can build up quickly, leading to CO poisoning.

CO poisoning is often called a "silent killer" because CO has no smell and you can't see it. Signals of CO poisoning include sleepiness, confusion, headache, dizziness, weakness and stomach upset. A person with CO poisoning needs fresh air and medical attention immediately!

To prevent CO poisoning, only use fuel-burning equipment for its intended use, and always operate it according to the manufacturer's instructions. For example, don't try to heat a house using a gas oven or cook food on a gas grill inside the house. If a fire occurs or equipment malfunctions leading to a buildup of CO in the home, properly working CO detectors can greatly reduce the family's risk of dying from CO poisoning. If the alarm goes off, get everyone outside and call 9-1-1 or the local emergency number!

Preventing Fires

For a fire to occur, three things must be present: fuel (something that burns), heat (something to catch the fuel on fire) and oxygen. One thing you can do to help prevent fires is to be extra careful with things that can cause a fire to start. Keep matches and lighters out of the reach of children, and never light candles, incense or oil lamps. Don't use space heaters unless the parents have instructed you to do so. If you are using a space heater, turn it off before you go to sleep or leave the area. Another step you can take to prevent fires is to keep things that burn (such as stuffed toys, curtains or clothing) at least 3 feet away from heat sources (such as stoves, fireplaces, grills or heaters) that could cause them to catch on fire.

Fires often start in the kitchen. Using kitchen appliances properly can help to prevent fires. Never leave items on the stove or in the oven unattended, and don't use aluminum foil or place metal objects in the microwave. Putting metal objects in the microwave causes sparking that could lead to a fire. If a kitchen fire does break out, you may be able to contain it:

- If a small fire starts in a pan on the stove, don't move it. Put on an oven mitt and slide a pan lid or cookie sheet on top of the pan to take away the air and put the fire out.

- Turn off the burner.

- Leave the lid on the pan until the pan is completely cool.

If the fire spreads to surrounding materials, leave the house and call 9-1-1 or the local emergency number from a safe location. If there is a fire in the oven, turn off the heat and keep the door closed. If there is a fire in the microwave, turn it off immediately. If you can safely reach the outlet, unplug it and keep the door closed. Leave the door closed until the fire is completely out.

Even a small kitchen fire can spread quickly. If you are in doubt, don't try to put it out. Just get yourself and the children out of the house and then call the fire department.

If a Fire Occurs

Your first priority is to get yourself and the children out. Don't worry about household belongings. Get out and stay out! As you are leaving, crawl low under smoke and test for hot doors before opening them. Once you are away from the fire, call 9-1-1 or the local emergency number. Never go back inside a burning building.

BE SMART, BE SAFE! Many fires that start on the stove are grease fires. You should never pour water on a grease fire, because this can cause the fire to spread. Don't use a fire extinguisher on a grease fire unless you are sure it is an ABC fire extinguisher. ABC fire extinguishers are safe to use with all types of fires. To use a fire extinguisher, remember PASS. (**Pull** the pin out, **Aim** at the base of the fire, **Squeeze** the handle and **Spray** side-to-side.)

Preventing Accidental Injuries

Accidental injuries, such as drowning, choking and poisoning, are the leading cause of death of children older than 1 year. Fortunately, there are lots of steps you can take to prevent accidental injuries. First, when you meet with the parents before taking a caregiving job, ask if you can go over the **Caregiver's Safety Inspection Checklist** with them. Then, take a copy of the checklist with you each time you work. Use it to help you recognize and prevent safety-related problems that you may run into on the job. You can download this tool from your online course. Second, always pay close attention to what the kids are doing. A lot of accidents can be prevented just by being alert. Finally, learn about how some common accidental injuries occur and what specific steps you can take to prevent them.

Preventing Burns

Children can easily be scalded by hot liquids or steam or burned by contact with flames or hot surfaces.

Many accidental burns occur in the kitchen, while food is being prepared or eaten. When you are working in the kitchen, keep the children within eyesight but out of high-traffic areas and away from appliances like the stove and microwave. For babies and toddlers, set up a secure play area or secure the baby or toddler in an infant seat, activity center or high chair. Never hold a child and cook, or hold a child while carrying hot foods or beverages. When you are using the stove, use the back burners and turn pot and pan handles toward the

BE SMART, BE SAFE!
Microwave ovens heat food and liquids unevenly, creating "hot spots." To avoid scald burns, always stir the contents of the container to distribute the heat. And never use a microwave to warm a baby bottle! The microwave heats the contents of the bottle unevenly and can make the liquid too hot in a very short amount of time.

back of the stove so that they are out of reach of little hands. Test the temperature of warmed bottles and baby food before serving it. When serving food to older children, allow the food to cool a bit before serving it, and place hot serving dishes (such as casseroles) at least 10 inches back from the table edge.

Bath time can also put a child at risk for scald burns. If you have been asked to give a child a bath, turn the hot water *on last* and *off first*. Before helping the child into the tub, test the water temperature by moving your hand back and forth in the water for several seconds to make sure

Hold the Phone!

We all love our mobile phones and tablets, but it's hard to keep an eye on kids while you're talking, texting or using the Internet. Use the phone for calls related to the job only, not for personal calls. Keep all conversations as short as possible, and keep the kids within eyesight while you are on the phone. Avoid texting or surfing while you are on the job, too. It's really easy to get so absorbed in what you are doing that you lose track of what the kids are doing. You might think it is OK to break out your mobile device or log onto the laptop once the kids are in bed, but it's really not. Even after kids are in bed, you need to be focused on keeping them safe. If you're caught up on a call with your friends, you could miss a child's call for help or other sounds that could indicate something is wrong. Remember, your first priority is always the kids, and you need to pay full attention to what they are doing!

the water is not too hot and that there are no hot spots. The bath water should not be any warmer than 100° F (39° C), which is a little warmer than body temperature. And of course you know never to leave a child alone in the bathroom. Not only is this a drowning risk, but a curious child might accidentally turn on the hot water tap and burn himself.

Burns can also occur from direct contact with flames. Keep children away from heat sources, such as stoves, fireplaces, grills and heaters. If a child's clothing catches on fire, have the child stop, drop and roll to put out the flames and minimize burns.

Preventing Electrical Shock

When an electrical current passes through the body, it can cause an electrical shock. Common causes of electrical shock in children include biting electrical cords and putting

metal objects, such as a fork, into an electrical outlet. An electric shock might just cause minor discomfort. But if the electric current is strong enough or contact is long enough, the child's heartbeat and breathing might be affected, putting the child at risk for dying. Contact with electricity can also cause burns where the electrical current enters and leaves the body.

To prevent electrical shocks, make sure all unused electrical outlets have safety covers. If you see that the child is interested in the electrical socket, remove her from the area and get her interested in another activity. Keep electrical cords out of the reach of children. Never use electrical appliances (such as hair dryers) near water, because water conducts electricity. If the appliance falls into the water, an electric shock could result.

Understanding Kids of All Ages: Keeping Kids Safe

Infant (Newborn to 12 months) 	■ Infants can easily roll or fall off surfaces. Always stay with an infant, keeping one hand on her at all times. Use safety straps on equipment such as changing tables and carriers. ■ Infants will put anything they can get their hands on in their mouths! Be alert to anything in the area that could be a potential choking hazard, including small toys (or parts of toys), and remove it. ■ Keep plastic bags and balloons away from infants. They could cause suffocation. ■ The only thing that should be in a crib with an infant is a mattress with a tight-fitting sheet. Blankets, pillows, stuffed animals and other soft, loose items are suffocation hazards. ■ Keep infants away from window cords, which could cause strangulation. ■ Never leave an infant alone near water, even a very small amount of water.
Toddler (1 to 3 years old) 	■ Toddlers have lots to see, do and explore. Never let a toddler out of your sight! ■ Toddlers have not outgrown putting things in their mouths, and they don't understand that things can hurt them. Poisoning and choking are big risks with this age group. ■ Keep toddlers away from window cords, which could cause strangulation. ■ Never leave a toddler alone near water, even a very small amount of water.
Preschooler (3 to 4 years old) 	■ Preschoolers have an increased ability to run, jump and climb, but they do not fully understand limits—so they may try to climb up, or jump off of, something that is too high, or they may run into a dangerous area. ■ Preschoolers enjoy doing arts and crafts projects and helping out with simple cooking projects. Make sure supplies are safe (for example, blunt safety scissors, nontoxic paints and glue, unbreakable bowls and cups).
Younger School-Age Child (5 to 7 years old) 	■ Younger school-age children are beginning to develop better judgment about what could hurt them, but they still need supervision to keep them safe. ■ Younger school-age children are active and enjoy playing in the yard and on the playground. As their physical abilities increase, they may test their limits, leading to injury. Younger school-age children are still learning about safety, so they may dash into the street to chase a ball without thinking. ■ Now that they are spending more time at school and playing in the neighborhood, younger school-age children need to be taught rules about talking to strangers. ■ Younger school-age children are still too young to cross the street by themselves.

Older School-Age Child (8 to 10 years old) 	■ Older school-age children have more knowledge about potentially dangerous situations and how to keep themselves safe.
	■ Older school-age children continue to be active. As with younger school-age children, rules about staying safe while playing outside may need to be reinforced.
	■ Older school-age children begin to develop hobbies and interests that may involve using tools, cooking equipment or chemicals. They may need help and supervision to complete certain projects safely.

Preventing Choking

Choking is a common cause of injury and death in children younger than 5 years. Choking occurs when the trachea (the passage through which air enters and leaves the lungs, sometimes called the "windpipe" or "airway") becomes either partially or completely blocked by food or a foreign object (such as a small toy). A child who is choking cannot speak or cry. He may cough weakly or not at all. He can quickly stop breathing, become unconscious and die. Later in this book, you will learn how to help a child or baby who is choking. But for now, let's look at how to prevent choking from happening in the first place.

There are many reasons kids have a high risk for choking. Babies and toddlers explore by putting things in their mouths and can easily choke on them. Even some common foods can be choking hazards in young children. For example, a young child can choke on small foods (such as nuts and seeds); round, firm foods (such as grapes, hot dogs and hard candies); and sticky foods (such as peanut butter). This is because children younger than 4 years do not have the skills needed to chew these foods thoroughly, so they often try to just swallow them whole. Laughing, talking or running with the mouth full can also lead to choking.

To lower the risk of choking during meal and snack times, always have the kids sit still to eat, and remind them not to talk or laugh with their mouths full. Feed babies and toddlers small spoonfuls of soft food that is easy to chew. Take your time, and give the baby or toddler time to swallow in between bites. When serving food to an older child, cut the food into bite-sized pieces (about ½ inch in size), and remind the child to take small bites and chew thoroughly before swallowing.

To lower the risk of choking during playtime, always make sure the kids are playing with toys that are safe and age-appropriate. Check toys such as stuffed animals and dolls to make sure that small parts (for example, buttons, eyes or noses) are securely attached. Clean up after playtime, especially if you are caring for an older child with a younger sibling, to prevent the younger child from having access to toys that could be choking hazards for her.

BE SMART, BE SAFE!

For babies and toddlers, no toy should be smaller than 1¾ inches in diameter. If you can fit the toy through a toilet paper tube, then it's too small!

Preventing Suffocation and Strangulation

Suffocation occurs whens something covers the child's nose and mouth, preventing the child from breathing, or when the child gets trapped in a small, enclosed space with limited oxygen (for example, a toy box, an old refrigerator, a cooler or a plastic storage container). Strangulation occurs when something tightens around the child's neck, cutting off his ability to breathe.

Plastic bags and latex balloons are suffocation hazards. A child can inhale an uninflated balloon or a piece of broken balloon which can then cover the opening of the windpipe and lead to suffocation. Soft objects in a baby's crib, including blankets, pillows and stuffed animals, can also pose a suffocation risk. A baby's crib should have nothing in it except a mattress with a tightly fitting sheet. If there is anything else in the crib, take it out! An older child can suffocate after becoming trapped

Choking Hazards

In children younger than 4 years, the following foods, household objects and toys may be choking hazards.

Foods

- Nuts and seeds (in fact, these should not be given to children younger than 7 years)

- Hot dogs or sausages

- Chunks of meat or cheese

- Chunks of fruit (such as apples) and whole grapes

- Raw vegetables (such as carrots and celery)

- Popcorn

- Peanut butter

- Hard, gooey or sticky candy (such as peppermint candies, fruit roll-ups, marshmallows, gummy bears and chewing gum)

- Large foods that break easily into small pieces (such as teething biscuits and cookies)

Household Objects and Toys

- Plastic bags, balloons and disposable gloves (which can get sucked into the airway)

- Coins

- Buttons

- Small "button" batteries (found inside watches, car key fobs, singing greeting cards, hearing aids and other electronics)

- Magnets

- Marbles

- Beads

- Pebbles

- Pen or marker caps

- Safety pins and hairpins

- Jewelry

- Baby powder

- Items from the trash (such as the pull tabs from soda cans)

- Toys meant for older children, which may be small or have small parts

in an enclosed space, such as a toy box or cooler (for example, during a game of hide and seek).

Strangulation can occur when a cord gets wrapped around a child's neck, or the child's head gets trapped (for example, between the slats of a crib or in between the posts on a railing or fence). Avoid dressing children in clothing with drawstrings, and remove a baby's or toddler's bib after the meal is finished. Keep drapery and blind cords wound up so that they do not dangle. Also, keep other items with strings, cords or ribbons (such as mobiles and corded baby monitors) out of reach.

Preventing Drowning

A child can drown in a very small amount of water (just an inch)! Pools, sinks, bathtubs, garbage cans and buckets, and even toilets and diaper pails are drowning hazards. Keep bathroom and laundry room doors closed and toilet lids down. Empty sinks and bathtubs of water when you are finished using them.

If you work at a home that has a swimming pool, hot tub or both, be sure that all gates, windows and doors leading to the pool or hot tub area are locked. Make sure hot tubs are covered and that the cover is secured. Keep pool toys out of the water and out of sight. A child may see a pool toy floating in the water and try to go after it. To prevent the child from climbing over a fence and getting into the pool or hot tub area, keep chairs, tables and other items the child could climb on away from the pool or hot tub enclosure. Never leave a child alone near the pool area, even if the gates are secure. If a child is missing, always

BE SMART, BE SAFE!
Young children are very curious, and their interests and abilites change from day to day. Do not leave a young child unattended near any source of water, even for a moment!

check the pool area first. Seconds count in preventing death or disability.

If there are bodies of water, fountains or other water features on or near the house where you are caregiving, tell children that these areas are off limits unless they are with you. If you are visiting another home with the children, check the site for potential water hazards and always supervise the children.

Circle of Drowning Prevention

Layers of protection are essential to help prevent drowning.
Plan ahead for aquatic activities:

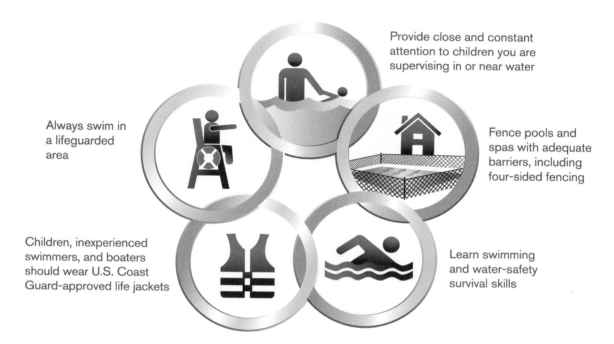

Provide close and constant attention to children you are supervising in or near water

Always swim in a lifeguarded area

Fence pools and spas with adequate barriers, including four-sided fencing

Children, inexperienced swimmers, and boaters should wear U.S. Coast Guard-approved life jackets

Learn swimming and water-safety survival skills

In general, it is best to avoid aquatic activities while caregiving. However, in some cases, parents may give you permission to take their children swimming. If you were hired to take care of children during the summer and the family has a home pool or a pool membership, you may be responsible for supervising children in and around water. Only take a child swimming if you have the parents' permission to do so, can swim well, are certified in CPR/AED, and are comfortable in and around the water. Layers of protection are *essential* to help prevent drowning. Plan ahead for aquatic activites.

General swimming safety

Never allow children to swim alone. Closely supervise children in, on or around water, no matter how well the child can swim or how shallow the water. Stay within an arm's reach of any weak or inexperienced swimmer who is in the water. Do not rely on the use of water wings, swim rings, inflatable toys and other items designed for water recreation to replace a U.S. Coast Guard-approved life jacket or adult supervision. These devices can suddenly shift position, lose air or slip out from underneath the child, putting the child at risk for drowning. They may also falsely increase a child's sense of confidence, causing him to venture into water that is too deep. Watch out for the "dangerous too's": too tired, too cold, too far from safety, too much sun and too much strenuous activity.

Know each child's swimming ability and make sure to follow specific rules (set by

the parents) for each child based on her swimming ability. Tell children to always enter the water feet-first, unless they are in an area that is clearly marked for diving and has no obstructions. Know where entry and exit points are. Make sure you have a means of summoning help (such as a mobile phone) close by. Aquatic emergencies often happen quickly and unexpectedly.

Do not allow children to engage in competitive underwater games, such as seeing who can hold their breath the longest underwater or seeing who can swim the farthest before coming up for air. Hyperventilation (that is, taking a series of rapid, deep breaths before submerging in an effort to hold the breath longer underwater) affects the body's drive to breathe. The child could pass out and then instinctively take a breath underwater, leading to drowning.

Even seemingly harmless kiddie pools pose danger. Only allow children to play in kiddie pools if you have the parents' permission. Always stay within arm's reach of a child near water, giving the child your undivided attention. If you must leave, take the child with you. Be sure to empty the kiddie pool when the kids are finished playing in it.

Swimming safety in a public pool

If you take the children to a public pool to swim, check the pool to see that it is well maintained. Reconsider letting the kids swim if you see obvious hazards, such as cracks in the deck, malfunctioning equipment or cloudy water. Also, do not allow the children to swim in a pool that is overly crowded or when other swimmers are not following the rules.

Trained lifeguards should be on duty at public pools. But even when lifeguards are present, you are still responsible for watching the children in your care and keeping them safe. Read all rules and posted signs, and explain the rules to the children, paying special attention to water-depth marking and "no diving" signs. Tell the children that they must obey the lifeguards' instructions at all times. Note the location of safety equipment (such as a reaching pole and ring buoy) and remind children not to play with the safety equipment. It is a good idea to have the children take breaks from swimming in order to rest.

Safety while bathing children

Bathing children is another high-risk activity involving water. Bathe children only if the parents have requested that you do so and only if you know how and feel comfortable giving a child a bath. If you are caregiving more than one child, do not give a bath to one of the children if you cannot properly keep an eye on all of the children. Also, be aware that bath seats and bath rings are not safety devices and will not help to prevent drowning.

BE SMART, BE SAFE! Never leave a child in a bathtub alone; always stay within arm's reach!

Preventing Poisoning

Children younger than 5 years, especially toddlers, are at the highest risk for poisoning. Children may be attracted to pretty liquids in bottles, sweet-smelling powders, berries on plants that look like they would taste good, or medications and vitamins that look like candy. And, as you have already learned, very young children explore their world by putting things in their mouths, so even things that don't look or smell attractive are poisoning hazards among this age group.

Practically anything can be a poison if it is not meant to be swallowed or inhaled. Even some things that are meant to be swallowed or inhaled, such as medications, can be poisonous if they are taken by the wrong person, or if the person takes too much. Keep all potential poisons locked away in cabinets, out of sight and out of reach of children. When it is not possible or practical to keep potential poisons locked away (for example, if there are houseplants in the house or plants out in the yard), closely watch children to make sure they don't get into something that they shouldn't. When you are using cleaning supplies, never leave the product where a child can gain access to it, and be sure to close the container tightly and put it away in a locked cabinet when you are finished using it. When you are doing arts and crafts projects with the kids, use nontoxic markers, glue and other art supplies.

Only give a child medicine if the parents have specifically told you to. Ask the parents to write down for you how much medication to give and when to give it. They can provide this information on the **Parental Consent and Contact Form**, which you can download from your online course. If you are responsible for giving the child medicine, read the label and make sure that you are giving the correct medication in the correct dosage. Write down what medicine you gave, the amount you gave and the time you gave it on your **Caregiver's Report Record**.

Danger! Poison!

Many everyday household items are poisonous if swallowed or inhaled. A curious child can get into something she shouldn't in no time. Always keep an eye on the kids when you are caregiving, and make sure potential poisons such as those on the following list are kept out of reach.

- Alcohol (found in mouthwash; perfume and cologne; after shave; vanilla extract; hand sanitizer; and of course, liquor, beer and wine)

- Medications (over-the-counter and prescription)

- Vitamins

- Lighter fluid

- Lamp oil

- Baby oil

- Make-up, hair and nail products

- Tobacco

- Cleaning and laundry products (detergent "pods" are especially attractive to kids)

- Paints

- Bug and weed killers

- Car maintenance products

- Plants (both houseplants and outdoor plants)

- Heavy metals, such as lead (a common source is old, peeling paint)

BE SMART, BE SAFE! When giving a child medicine, you should never refer to the medicine as "candy." It's important for kids to know the difference between medicine and candy.

Preventing Falls

Children, especially toddlers who are learning to walk, fall a lot. Frequently, falls are not serious and result only in a bump or a bruise. But if a baby or child falls from a height, more serious injuries (like broken bones or head injuries) can occur. To help prevent more serious falls from occurring:

- Never leave babies or young children alone on changing tables, high chairs, booster seats, beds, couches or other pieces of furniture.

- Always use the safety straps on changing tables, high chairs and booster seats.

- Keep high chairs away from the table and away from counters and walls. The child could push off the table, counter or wall and tip over in the high chair.

- Keep babies and young children away from stairs, and make sure that safety gates and doors that lead to stairs are closed. Keep stairs clear of clutter.

- Prevent children from climbing onto furniture or other high surfaces. Push chairs in underneath tables and desks, and put away stools or ladders.

- Prevent children from gaining access to windows. Keep furniture the child could climb on away from windows, and keep windows locked. Window screens are not strong enough to hold a child in if he starts to fall, and a child can fall from a window that is only opened 4 inches.

4

PLAYING WITH KIDS OF ALL AGES

Caregiving involves a lot of responsibility—making sure to follow the parents' rules, being a role model, keeping kids safe—it's a lot of work (and we haven't even gotten to other caregiver responsibilities, like changing diapers, yet!). However, the job can also be fun! As a caregiver, you're being paid to have fun with the kids. Let's talk a little bit about playing with kids.

Play: It's a Tough Job

The main job of young children is to play. Through play, children develop muscle strength, coordination and dexterity. They learn about the world around them. And they learn how to express their feelings, solve problems and get along with others. Playing helps children learn and grow physically, mentally, socially and emotionally.

- **Physical development.** Activities that use the big muscles of the body, like running, jumping and dancing, help kids grow stronger and become more coordinated, so that they can eventually do more complex activities, like riding a bike. Activities that use the small muscles of the body, like putting beads on a string and coloring, help children develop the skills they need for more difficult tasks like writing and fastening buttons.

- **Mental development.** Activities like learning rhymes, singing songs, doing puzzles, sorting and naming things, counting and reading help children learn about their world and develop memory and concentration skills. Play activities that encourage kids to use their imagination help them to develop creative thinking skills.

- **Social development.** Following rules, taking turns while playing a game, playing on a sports team or playing an instrument in a band are activities that help children learn how to get along with others and be part of a group.

- **Emotional development.** Activities like playing make-believe, acting out a skit and asking "what if" questions help children to learn about and express their feelings.

Types of Play

There are many types of play. All benefit kids in different ways.

- **Active play** allows kids to burn off extra energy. Playing games like tag or hula hooping, riding bikes, playing catch and climbing on monkey bars are examples of active play.

- **Quiet play** helps kids to calm down. Reading a book, doing a puzzle, coloring, or playing with dolls or stuffed animals are examples of quiet play.

- **Constructive play** involves making or building things. Constructive play lets kids use their creativity. Examples of constructive play include arts and crafts projects, playing with building blocks and making a pillow fort.

- **Fantasy play** gives kids a chance to use their imagination. Acting out pretend scenarios with dolls, action figures or stuffed animals; dressing up in costumes; or putting on a skit or a puppet show are examples of fantasy play.

- **Social play** means playing with other children or adults (or both). Social play allows children to develop the skills they need to get along with others, such as how to communicate, how to share, how to work as part of a team to achieve a goal and how to handle disagreements.

How to Play with Kids

Keeping the kids entertained and happy is a little like being a cruise director on a ship. If you've ever been on a cruise, you know that the cruise director is the person in charge of fun. His or her job is to plan activities and entertainment and to make sure that the passengers on the cruise have a great time on their vacation. In much the same way, one of your jobs while you are caregiving is to make sure the kids have fun. By the way, this benefits you too—happy, busy kids are easier to watch and less likely to get into trouble than grumpy, bored ones!

When thinking about ways to keep the kids you are caregiving entertained, the first thing you need to do is know your audience. As children grow older, they develop new skills and their interests and the activities they enjoy change.

Choosing toys and activities that match the child's stage of development helps to prevent the child from becoming frustrated, and it also helps you to keep the child safe.

Kids may also differ a little bit in what they enjoy depending on whether they are boys or girls. However, be careful about assuming that *all* boys or *all* girls act a certain way or like the same things. Some girls may enjoy playing with cars. Some boys may like to play with dolls. Get to know each child as an individual, and appreciate what makes him or her unique. Also, keep in mind that there are many activities, such as reading books and playing games, that most kids like to do regardless of whether they are girls or boys.

Understanding Kids of All Ages: Keeping Kids Entertained

Infant

(Newborn to 12 months)

Infants:

- Begin showing interest in people, especially faces and voices, around the age of 2 to 3 months.

- Do not play directly with other children, but older infants are very interactive with other children and adults.

- Learn about their world with their hands, mouths and eyes.

Infants younger than 6 months enjoy:

- Toys with bright primary colors, high contrast (for example, black and white) and simple designs.

- Mobiles.

- Soft dolls, stuffed animals and squeeze toys.

- Play mirrors.

- Objects they can explore with their hands and mouths, such as plastic keys on a ring.

- Looking at picture books and listening to stories.

Infants older than 6 months enjoy:

- Floor activity centers and activity quilts.

- Toys that move or make noise.

- Toys that can open and shut and contain items.

- Toys that can be stacked, pushed or pulled.

  - Toys that can be squeezed, dropped, poked, twisted or thrown.

    - Hidden-object toys and games like peek-a-boo.

  - Looking at picture books and listening to stories.

Toddler	**Toddlers:**	**Toddlers enjoy:**
(1 to 3 years old) 	■ Are very physically active and busy and are developing the ability to walk, run, climb, go up and down stairs and jump. ■ May play beside other toddlers but rarely play with each other until they get closer to preschool age. ■ Become easily frustrated with toys or activities that are too advanced for them. ■ Have short attention spans and become easily bored. ■ Are beginning to show an interest in the physical qualities of things, such as an object's texture, shape, size and color.	■ Handling and carrying around dolls, stuffed animals and action figures. ■ Simple dress-up play (for example, fancy or funny hats). ■ Toys that can be pushed, pulled or make noise. ■ Playing with toys in pretend scenes that are familiar and realistic (such as farms or parking lots). ■ Toys with bright colors that look real. ■ Lugging, dumping, pushing, pulling, piling up, knocking down, emptying and filling things. ■ Large balls that can be rolled and kicked. ■ Showing off physical skills, such as climbing, hanging from arms, rolling and galloping. ■ Arranging things by number, size or other pattern (by 2 years of age). ■ Hidden-object toys. ■ Looking at picture books and listening to stories.

Preschooler

(3 to 4 years old)

Preschoolers:

- Like imaginary situations and have toys that are close companions.

- Play well with other children and are learning how to share and take turns.

- Understand the difference between what is "mine," "his" and "hers."

- Are learning the concept of fair play but are not quite ready for competitive play.

Preschoolers enjoy:

- Playing make-believe and dress-up.

- Pretend toys (for example, play money, play kitchen sets).

- Puppets.

- Stuffed animals and dolls.

- Building things.

- Simple arts and crafts projects, like coloring or making bracelets out of cereal.

- Toys with realistic detail and working parts.

- Cars, play scenes and small figures.

- Simple board games.

- Outside games with simple rules like Duck Duck Goose and Red Light, Green Light.

- Physical activities such as running, jumping, climbing, catching, throwing, kicking and riding tricycles.

- Looking at picture books and listening to stories.

| **Younger School-Age Child**

(5 to 7 years old)

 | **Younger school-age children:**

■ Have an increased ability to play cooperatively and enjoy group activities.

■ Are able to follow games with more complex rules and have a strong sense of fair play.

■ Prefer to play with children of the same gender.

■ Are beginning to develop interests such as nature and simple science, music and collecting. | **Younger school-age children enjoy:**

■ Arts and crafts kits.

■ Puppets.

■ Jump ropes.

■ Miniature dolls and action figures.

■ Secret languages and passwords.

■ Simple games involving numbers, time, calendars and the value of coins.

■ Spelling activities and games.

■ Reading. |
| **Older School-Age Child**

(8 to 10 years old)

 | **Older school-age children:**

■ Are beginning to develop lifelong skills and hobbies and enjoy team sports.

■ Are beginning to learn how to lose gracefully. | **Older school-age children enjoy:**

■ Video games and handheld electronic games.

■ Board games.

■ Sports equipment.

■ Model kits.

■ Musical instruments.

■ Magic sets.

■ Chemistry sets.

■ Reading. |

Kids often look forward to a caregiver's visit, because they know that the caregiver will have the time to play with them. Kids *really* look forward to visits from caregivers who know how to have fun! Before you go on a caregiving job, think about the kids you will be caregiving and some activities they might enjoy. For some great ideas, see Appendix C: Fun Activities for Kids. If you plan a specific activity to do with the kids, like doing an arts and crafts project or making a special treat, be sure to discuss your plans with the parents beforehand and get their OK. They may have the supplies you need for your activity already, or you may need to bring the supplies along. And it's never a bad idea to throw some extra fun surprises that are appropriate for the children you are caregiving in your caregiving bag before you go! For example, if you will be caregiving a preschooler, you could take along a new coloring book and crayons.

Kids *really* look forward to visits from caregivers who know how to have fun!

It's always good to be prepared with some ideas, but don't get too upset if the kids want to do something else. As long as whatever they want to do is safe and doesn't break any of the parents' rules, then just go with it and have fun.

While you play with the children, watch how they act, learn what activities they like best and discover how they want to play.

Play It Safe

Just because you're having fun with the kids doesn't mean you can forget about safety. Keep kids safe during play by watching them at all times. Make sure the environment is safe and that whatever they are doing is within the parents' rules for play (check your notes on the **Family Interview Form**). If the kids start to get wound up and their playing gets rough, change the activity to something calmer to settle them down.

When helping kids decide what toy or game to play with or what activity to do, keep their ages and abilities in mind. Safety depends on the right toy or activity at the right age. Remember to read all directions and warnings on children's toys and games to find out the recommended ages and how to use them properly. If a child wants to play with an inappropriate toy or game, explain why he cannot play with it and suggest another fun activity.

Playing It Safe on the Playground and at the Park

Some parents may say it is OK for you to take the kids to a nearby park or playground to burn off some extra energy. Here are some safety considerations to be aware of when kids are playing on a playground or in a park:

- Check the equipment to make sure it is in good condition. Look for openings or railings that could trap a child's hands, head or feet. Any space larger than the width of a soda can is unsafe.

- Check for sand, pea gravel, shredded rubber, wood chips or rubber matting under play equipment to cushion falls.

- Don't let kids wear clothing or accessories that could get caught in the equipment, such as clothing with drawstrings, necklaces and scarves. Make sure they are wearing shoes that will stay on, like sneakers.

- Check that the sand in sandboxes is clean and safe.

- Check for any water in the area, such as a fountain, pond or a lake. Don't let the kids play near the water.

- Never let the kids out of your sight!

Born to Ride: Safety Tips for Kids on Bikes, Scooters, Skateboards and Other Toys with Wheels

If the parents have given you the OK to let kids play outside with riding toys, you will need to take some extra precautions to keep them safe:

- Dress the kids in bright colors so that they can easily be seen.

- Make sure their clothes fit well and and that shoelaces are snugly tied. Otherwise, their clothing or shoelaces could get caught in wheels or other moving parts.

- Have the kids wear appropriate protective gear, such as helmets, knee pads and elbow pads, when using bicycles, skateboards, scooters and other riding toys.

- Teach the kids to be careful and to sit where they should when driving a battery-powered riding toy.

- Don't let kids play with riding toys, bikes, skateboards or scooters near pools, on hilly or steep ground, in streets, on steps or around parked cars.

- Never let the kids out of your sight!

FROM FEEDING TO BEDTIME: CARING FOR KIDS

5

Chances are, you decided to start caregiving because you liked the idea of helping with kids. Maybe you are the oldest child in your family and have been helping to feed, dress and change your younger brothers or sisters for as long as you can remember. Or maybe you have successfully raised two kids and really miss being around small children. As a caregiver, you will put these skills to use. One important (and obvious!) responsibility you will have as a caregiver is to provide basic child care, including feeding kids, dressing kids and keeping kids clean.

Following Care Routines

Routines develop around events that happen on a regular basis, like meals and bedtime. Every family has its own routines. For example, some families may give thanks before they eat or sing a special bedtime song every night. When you meet with the family before taking a caregiving job, always ask about when they do things, how they do things, and what products and equipment they use, and make a note of these instructions on your **Family Interview Form**. Try to follow the family's normal routines as closely as you can—kids are usually happiest this way!

Parents will also appreciate knowing what went on while they were away. For example, what time did the kids go to bed or down for a nap, and did they wake up at all? What did you give them to eat, and how much did they eat? How many times did you need to change the infant's diaper? Filling out a **Caregiver's Report Record** is an easy way to keep track of these details for the parents. (You can download a blank Caregiver's Report Record from your online course.)

Watching Out for Germs

We've all seen the signs in public restrooms—"Employees must wash hands before returning to work!" Well, when you are caring for children, you are an employee of the family. You have a responsibility to keep the family safe from illnesses, such as colds and the flu, that are caused by germs. You also need to keep yourself safe from germs you might pick up from the family!

Germs are spread by direct contact with another person's body fluids (such as blood, mucus, urine or feces) and by contact with objects or surfaces that have been contaminated with germs (for example, a remote control that a person with a cold has handled). Germs can also be spread through the air when a person who is sick coughs or sneezes.

Even if a person does not appear to be sick, he can still spread germs. For example, you know that small kids will touch anything and everything. They can then pass the germs they pick up on their hands to others. The single most important thing you can do to prevent the spread of germs is to wash your hands frequently and to encourage the kids in your care to do the same! You should also use disposable gloves to protect yourself from germs when you are providing care that involves coming into direct contact with a child's body fluids.

Slowing the Spread of Germs

There are several things you can do to slow the spread of germs and help keep yourself and the kids you care for healthy:

- Wash your hands frequently, and encourage the kids to do the same! At minimum, hands should be washed before preparing food and eating, after going to the bathroom, after coughing or sneezing, after coming in from playing outside, after playing with pets and whenever hands are visibly dirty. You should also wash your hands after changing a diaper or giving first aid.

- Eat healthy foods, get plenty of rest, and exercise regularly. These healthy habits help your body fight infection.

- If you feel sick or are ill, do not work. Hopefully, parents will extend the same courtesy to you and not ask you to work when one of the kids is sick!

- Use tissues and cover your mouth and nose when coughing and sneezing. If you don't have a tissue, cough or sneeze into the inside of your elbow. Teach the kids to do the same.

- Keep toys and play areas clean.

- Wear disposable gloves when providing care that involves contact with body fluids such as urine, feces, blood or vomit.

Hand Washing

Hand washing is *the most important thing* you can do to to help prevent the spread of germs. Washing hands frequently and for at least 20 seconds is key! Use warm water, and work up a good lather. Be sure to wash the palms and backs of the hands, between the fingers and underneath the fingernails. For step-by-step instructions on washing hands, see Skill Sheet 5-1 (Hand Washing) on page 99.

If you don't have soap and water, you can use hand sanitizer to remove germs from hands. To use hand sanitizer, apply the product to the palm of one hand (check the label to see how much to use—it spreads out, but you need enough to cover both hands). Then, rub the hands together to spread the product over the backs and palms of both hands, in between the fingers and underneath the fingernails. Keep rubbing until your hands are dry. Hand sanitizer works best when hands aren't really grimy, so if you can see whatever is making the hands dirty or if they just feel gross, find some soap and water!

Scrub Up!

Always wash your hands:

- Before and after you prepare food.

- Before and after you eat.

- Before and after changing diapers or helping a child to use the toilet.

- After using the toilet.

- After coughing, sneezing or blowing your nose.

- After handling garbage.

- After cleaning up spills.

- After playing outdoors.

- After touching animals or insects, or their droppings.

- After touching plants.

- Before and after giving first aid.

Make sure the kids wash their hands:

- Before and after they eat.

- After using the toilet or having a diaper changed (wash the baby's hands for her).

- After touching objects or surfaces used by other people in public areas.

- After playing outdoors.

- After coughing, sneezing or blowing their noses.

- After touching or handling animals or insects, or their droppings.

- After touching plants.

Using Disposable Gloves

Wear disposable gloves to protect yourself from germs whenever you are providing care that involves coming into contact with another person's body fluids. For example, you should put on disposable gloves before changing a diaper, giving first aid for a scraped knee or helping a child who is vomiting. Many families will not have disposable gloves available, so you should keep some in your caregiver's bag and first aid kit. You can buy disposable gloves at the drugstore or grocery store. Disposable gloves come in different sizes; buy the size that fits your hands. Gloves that are too big are difficult to work in, and gloves that are too small may tear. Look for disposable gloves that are made of vinyl or nitrile, not latex, because many people are sensitive to latex and can have an allergic reaction to it.

Disposable gloves are worn once and thrown away. You need to remove and dispose of the gloves properly after you use them to avoid spreading germs onto your hands or other surfaces. After removing and throwing away your gloves, wash your hands!

For step-by-step instructions on removing disposable gloves, see Skill Sheet 5-2 (Removing Disposable Gloves) on page 100.

Handling a Crying Baby

If you will be caring for babies, you need to know what to do when the baby cries. Crying is a baby's way of communicating everything: hunger, thirst, a dirty diaper or other source of discomfort, even boredom. It's also natural for babies to cry even when nothing is wrong. A baby normally spends 1 to 3 hours of each day crying!

Colic

Colic is a condition in which an otherwise healthy baby cries for more than 3 hours a day, more than 3 days a week. During a crying episode, the baby's face may turn red and her belly may be tense and hard. She may clench her legs, feet and fists. The crying episodes usually occur at the same time each day, often in the early evening. Babies who have colic usually outgrow it by the age of 3 months, but it can continue up to the age of 1 year. Nobody knows for sure what causes colic, but some theories include gas, a food sensitivity or allergy, or being overwhelmed or exhausted.

A colicky baby can be a challenge for even the most experienced caregiver. Be sure to ask the parents if their baby has colic before you agree to care for kids.

When the baby starts to cry, first check the basics:

- Does she need a diaper change?

- Is she hungry?

- Is it getting close to naptime or bedtime? (Maybe she is just tired.)

- Is she too hot or too cold? (If you feel too hot or cold, chances are the baby feels the same way! In general, the baby should have on about the same amount of clothing as you do. If you are concerned that the baby is cold, add one more light layer, but don't overdo it.)

- Is something causing her pain or discomfort? For example, is she teething? Does she have a diaper rash? Is she feverish?

You may not ever find a reason why the baby is crying. This is when it is useful to have some tricks up your sleeve for calming a crying baby.

Shaken Baby Injuries

Never shake a baby or young child, not even in play! Babies and young children have weak neck muscles and heavy heads. Shaking a baby or young child causes the head to flop back and forth, which can lead to severe injuries ranging from brain damage to death.

Shaken baby injuries are most common in children younger than 2 years. Often, these injuries occur when a caregiver becomes frustrated with a baby's crying or an older child's behavior and shakes the baby or child to get him to stop. Gentle shaking can quickly turn into violent shaking when a person is feeling frustrated or angry. No matter how frustrated or angry you feel, never shake a baby or a child! If you feel like you are losing control of your emotions, put the baby or child in a safe place (such as in her crib) and try to calm down. If necessary, call someone you trust and ask for help dealing with the situation.

It can be frustrating when you've tried everything you can think of to get a crying baby to stop crying, but the crying doesn't stop. If you find yourself becoming annoyed or angry with the baby, gently put him in his crib on his back, leave the room and try to calm yourself down. Be sure to check on him every 5 to 10 minutes. If you need to, call the child's parents or someone you trust and ask for help.

Soothing a Crying Baby

Try the tricks below to calm a crying baby.

Gentle Motions

- Rock in a rocking chair while holding the baby.

- Walk or gently sway back and forth while holding the baby.

- Push the baby in a stroller or baby swing.

Soothing Sounds

Position the baby so that he can hear:

- A loudly ticking clock.

- Running or dripping water from a faucet or shower.

- A running fan, air conditioner, dishwasher, washing machine, dryer or vacuum cleaner.

- A recording of waterfalls or ocean waves.

- Lullabies or classical music.

Fun Things to Watch

Position the baby so that she can see:

- The swinging pendulum of a grandfather clock.

- A revolving ceiling fan.

- A fish tank.

- Running water.

- Leaves on trees.

- Moving cars.

- Children playing.

Understanding Kids of All Ages: Helping Kids with Daily Care

Infant (Newborn to 12 months) 	■ Infants younger than 6 months are not able to support their own heads. ■ In the space of 1 year, infants go from being unable to even sit up on their own to sitting, crawling and being able to stand and take a few wobbly steps.
Toddler (1 to 3 years old) 	■ Toddlers are able to drink from a cup and are learning how to feed themselves (with their hands at first, and then with a small spoon). ■ Toddlers are able to dress themselves (with lots of help). ■ Toddlers begin learning how to use the potty. ■ Toddlers can wash and dry their hands, using a toddler step stool that allows them to reach the sink.
Preschooler (3 to 4 years old) 	■ Preschoolers are on the way to being toilet-trained, but may still need to wear a diaper or training pants at night. ■ Preschoolers are able to wash their own hands and face. ■ Preschoolers can dress and undress themselves with some help. By the age of 4 years, preschoolers can tie their shoes with help.
Younger School-Age Child (5 to 7 years old) 	■ Younger school-age children are becoming more coordinated, which allows them to dress, bathe (with supervision) and eat on their own.
Older School-Age Child (8 to 10 years old) 	■ Older school-age children are more independent and able to do most things for themselves, but they may still need reminders to do a thorough job!

Picking Up and Holding Children

If you care for babies and toddlers, you will need to know how to pick them up and hold them safely. Most children enjoy being held, although some do not. When you meet with the family before taking a caregiving job, remember to ask the parents how their children like to be picked up and held, and write down their answers on the Family Interview Form.

Babies

There are several ways to pick up and hold a baby. The most important thing to remember when you are picking up and holding a baby is that you need to support the baby's head and neck when the baby is younger than 6 months old. Young babies have large heads and weak neck muscles, so they aren't able to support the weight of their heads on their own. They need your help!

One way to pick up a baby is to slide both of your hands under the baby's underarms, wrapping your fingers around the baby's ribs, and then gently lift. Another way to pick up a baby is to slide one hand under the baby's head and back and the other hand under the baby's bottom. Then gently lift. For step-by-step instructions on picking up babies, see Skill Sheet 5-3 (Picking Up an Infant) on page 101.

BE SMART, BE SAFE!

Babies are heavy! To avoid straining your back, get as close to the baby as you can before you lift her. If the baby is lying in a crib, slide her to the side closest to you and then lift her up. If the baby is lying on the floor or in a stroller, kneel down to get close to the baby before lifting her up.

Once you've picked the baby up, you need to hold her securely. The baby may arch her back and throw her head back suddenly, which could cause you to lose your grip! In addition, holding a baby close to your body helps the baby feel safe and secure, so it is calming for the baby.

- **Shoulder hold.** A shoulder hold works well if you are walking with a baby or trying to calm a baby. In a shoulder hold, the baby is leaning against your chest, looking over your shoulder. Put one arm under the baby's bottom and the other arm along her back, with your hand supporting her head and neck.

- **Cradle hold.** A cradle hold lets the baby look at your face; this is a good way to hold a baby when you are talking to him, entertaining him with funny faces or feeding him. To hold a baby in a cradle hold, support the baby's back along one arm, with his head resting in the crook of your elbow. Use your other arm to support the baby's bottom and legs.

For step-by-step instructions on holding babies, see Skill Sheet 5-4 (Holding an Infant) on page 102.

Toddlers

Most toddlers like to be picked up and held, but some do not. You should only pick up a toddler if you can support the toddler's weight and the parents say it is OK. When picking up a toddler, bend at your knees. Slide both of your hands under the toddler's underarms, wrapping your hands around the toddler's ribs. Stand up, using your legs to lift yourself and the toddler up in a smooth, continuous motion.

BE SMART, BE SAFE!

Never bend over at the waist to pick up a toddler. You could injure your back this way. Instead, bend at your knees and use the strong muscles in your legs to power yourself and the toddler up.

Once you've lifted the toddler up, you can hold her in an upright position facing you, putting one arm under her bottom for support and the other arm across her back. Don't hold the toddler on one hip, because this can strain your back. Instead, hold her in front of you with her legs wrapped around your waist. You can also sit with the toddler on your lap to give her a bottle or drink from a spill-proof cup, or to read to her. Just be sure to pay close attention because a toddler is likely to scoot off your lap if she sees something she wants to investigate!

For step-by-step instructions on picking up and a toddler, see Skill Sheet 5-5 (Picking Up and Holding a Toddler) on page 103.

Feeding Children

The parents may ask you to give a baby a bottle, feed a toddler or serve a meal or snack to older children. Get details from the parents about when, what and how much to feed their children. Parents of infants will typically leave specific instructions and a feeding schedule. For toddlers and older children, pay special attention to what foods and drinks the kids are allowed to have, and when they are allowed to have them. Write down the parents' instructions regarding meals, drinks and snacks on the Family Interview Form.

Food Allergies

Make a special point to ask the parents if the child has any food allergies. If the child you are caring for has a food allergy, you must be vigilant. Be careful about cross contact. Clean eating surfaces thoroughly, make sure to wash your hands, and have the child wash her hands with soap and water before eating or touching her face. Never let the child share cups, utensils, bottles or dishes with anyone, even her siblings. Because it can be dangerous to give outside food to a child with allergies, be sure to ask the parents whether it's alright if you bring your own food into the house. Some children will even react to the scent of an allergen, so the parents may ask you not to bring any food into the home at all. If you are on an outing with the child, do not let her eat, or even touch, store-bought foods or foods prepared by another family. Many foods have hidden ingredients. Be sure to carry any necessary medications or

an epinephrine auto injector with you in case the child is exposed to the food. See Chapter 8 for more information about how to recognize and what to do in case of an allergic reaction!

BE SMART, BE SAFE!

If you are caring for a child who has a food allergy, ask the parents to write down exactly what to do if the child is accidentally exposed to the food to which she is allergic! Make sure you know what medications to give, how to give them, and where they are located in the house!

Parent Preferences

Good nutrition often is influenced by food habits acquired in childhood. Family food preferences and behaviors strongly influence children's likes, dislikes and eating patterns. Children generally learn to enjoy a wide variety of foods if they are exposed to them in pleasant situations. You can help children in your care establish good eating habits and wholesome attitudes toward food. These attitudes will affect their health throughout their entire lives.

Parents will differ greatly on the types of foods they allow their children to eat. Some families are vegetarian or vegan and will only have plant-based foods in the home. Other families follow a kosher

Preventing Food Poisoning

Food poisoning can occur after eating foods or drinking fluids that are contaminated with germs. Preparing and storing food properly can help to prevent food poisoning.

- Wash your hands before you prepare food.

- Wash raw fruits and vegetables carefully before eating them or feeding them to the kids.

- Never let the kids eat cookie dough or brownie batter. Cookie dough and brownie batter contain raw eggs, which can make a person sick.

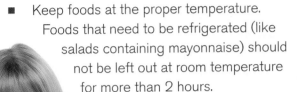

- Keep foods at the proper temperature. Foods that need to be refrigerated (like salads containing mayonnaise) should not be left out at room temperature for more than 2 hours.

- Don't put half-finished baby bottles or dishes of baby food back in the refrigerator. Germs from the child's mouth can grow in the leftovers, causing them to spoil.

diet, a gluten-free diet or a diet without processed foods. Other families eat a diet that includes some healthy and some not so healthy foods. It is your job to follow the dietary instructions of the parents and to feed the children with whatever food is available in the home (unless part of your job is to shop for food). However, meal planning provides a great opportunity for you to model good nutritional habits by bringing your own foods to eat while working. Ask the parents if their child can try some of your healthy snacks and talk to the child about how nutritious foods help kids stay strong and healthy.

Never buy the child a food treat that the parents do not allow. For example, if you are out with the child, she may see an ice cream shop and beg you to stop. You want to make her happy, but the parents have instructed that they do not want their child to have sugary treats during

the day. Instead of just saying no, create excitement by telling the child that you will help her make a yummy snack back at the house.

Nutritious Meal Planning

Although the parents will buy the food, you will often be responsible for creating snacks and meals from what is available. It is important to understand developmental concepts of nutrition and the basics of balanced meals in order to help you plan the best and most nutritious snacks and meals for children.

Developmental concepts of good nutrition

In general, healthy infants have good appetites. Children's appetites decrease toward the end of their first year and continue to decrease in their second year as growth slows down. Toddlers may show their need for independence by choosing not to eat. Preschool children frequently eat smaller meals and may want to snack between meals. Children who are 3 or 4 years old may eat slowly but generally eat more at one sitting than younger children do. By age 6, most children have developed stable, healthy appetites.

Infants

Infants typically receive feedings of breast milk or formula. Cereal usually is not introduced until the infant is around 5 to 6 months of age. Offer the infant a bottle of breast milk or formula before any solid meal. Solid food should be a supplement, not a replacement, for breast milk or formula.

When giving an infant cereal, start with 2 tablespoons of rice cereal twice daily and then introduce other single-grain cereals one at a time. Introduce multigrain cereal last. Giving the baby only one new food at a time allows him to get used to the flavor and makes it easier to determine whether he is allergic to any particular type of food. During feedings, the baby may push most of the cereal out of his mouth as a result of the tongue's normal sucking action. Use the spoon to gently put the food back into his mouth. To prevent overfeeding or choking, never put cereal into the baby's bottle.

As the infant reaches 6 to 8 months of age, he may begin to hold the bottle of formula. However, you need to continue to hold the infant during feedings to increase his sense of security and to meet his social needs. Gradually, apple and noncitrus juices are introduced one at a time. Solid foods such as strained fruits, vegetables and meats are added. Again, introduce new foods one at a time. When using commercially prepared baby food, spoon a meal-sized portion into a bowl, and refrigerate the unused food for up to 24 hours. Feeding the infant directly from the jar introduces bacteria into the jar and contaminates the uneaten portion, which must be thrown away. Never sweeten foods with honey because unpasteurized honey can cause botulism in infants.

Around the age of 9 to 12 months, children begin to drink liquids from a cup. Continue feeding the child cereal and slowly advance to chunkier toddler foods. During meals, give the child a separate spoon to encourage self-feeding skills. Introduce small finger foods, such as nonsugared adult cereals, cooked vegetables and fruits. Avoid giving the child nuts, raw vegetables, popcorn, grapes and hard candy, which can easily

DID YOU KNOW?

Keep in mind that the following sections cover general developmental guidelines for good nutrition. As a caregiver, make sure you ask for, and follow, detailed instructions from the parents about when, what and how much to feed their children.

lodge in the throat and cause choking. Make sure the child eats foods such as biscuits, toast and crackers while sitting up (never while lying down) to reduce the possibility of choking on crumbs.

Toddlers

Toddlers are beginning to be weaned from bottle- or breast-feeding and are getting used to drinking from a cup instead. Keep in mind that stress of illness or injury can lead the child to regress to a previous behavior. Do not be surprised if a child who was no longer drinking from a bottle begins to do so again.

Milk intake in a toddler typically is limited to 16 to 24 ounces daily to encourage the child to eat solid food. Avoid giving the toddler very spicy foods, which can be hard for a young child to digest.

Use the child's appetite to gauge how much to serve at mealtime. Typical serving sizes for a 2- to 3-year-old child include 2 to 3 tablespoons of applesauce or cooked vegetables; ¼ of a banana or apple; ⅓ cup of orange juice; 1 to 2 ounces of meat, fish or poultry; ½ slice of bread; ⅓ cup of cooked dry peas, beans or lentils; and 2 to 3 tablespoons of rice or cereal. Make mealtimes fun and encourage the child to use his own cup and spoon while eating. Never force a child to eat or use food as a reward or punishment.

Toddlers are known to be picky eaters. They may eat only one type of food for several days. They also like to "eat and run." Continue to present the child with a balanced diet by offering nutritious between-meal snacks such as cubed cheese and bread or unsalted crackers spread with peanut butter.

BE SMART, BE SAFE!
To prevent choking, do not give toddlers small, round or hard foods, such as hot dogs or hard candy!

Preschoolers

The quality of a preschooler's diet is more important than the quantity. Continue to offer a balanced diet, serving the child approximately 1 tablespoon of each food for each year of his age. You may introduce low-fat or skim milk at this time. A preschool child needs the calcium supplied by two to three 8-ounce servings of milk each day but may not be able to drink an entire serving of milk at one time. To make sure the child gets enough calcium, serve him milk and dairy products as snacks.

Cheese cut into cubes and served with fruit or crackers makes an ideal snack, as do cheese spreads on crackers or bread. Avoid serving cream cheese, which is high in fat and is more like butter than cheese. Cottage cheese with fruit or plain low-fat yogurt with fruit added at home is another good snack choice.

To increase the child's iron and protein intake include snacks from the meat group. Cut leftover cooked meat into cubes and serve with a fruit or vegetable. Another high-protein snack is hard-cooked eggs served with cheese. Offer sweet, high-fat or salty foods *only* after meeting basic nutrition requirements. Try serving the child yogurt, raisins and graham crackers instead of sweet desserts.

School-age children and adolescents

In the early school-age years, children grow less rapidly than they do in the later school-age years, as they approach puberty. Children's appetites often reflect these differences. Encourage the child to assist with meal planning to promote

control and independence. When serving meals, expect to increase the portion size of each food served according to how much the child will eat, and continue to offer a balanced diet.

During the school-age years, a child's food choices and preferences are often influenced by his peers and by television commercials. Luckily, most children seem to have an avid interest in food and this is a good time to teach them how to make healthy food choices. Encouraging a child to choose nutritious snacks is a good way to promote his sense of independence.

When planning meals for an adolescent, be aware that adolescents need more protein and iron, which help the body as it continues to grow and mature. Iron is especially important for adolescent girls who begin to menstruate at this time. Peers and personal body image influence food selection during adolescence. Eating a balanced diet during adolescence is important for promoting good nutrition and maintaining health in the adult years.

Basics of balanced meals and snacks

The United States Department of Agriculture (USDA) created a tool to help adults plan nutritious snacks and meals for children. ChooseMyPlate is a great visual that shows what the meal plate should look like proportionally. (See image on previous page.) Half of the plate should filled with vegetables and fruits. The other half is filled with grains and protein. Half of the grains served should be whole grains, like oatmeal or brown rice. Dairy, in the form of whole milk (for children up to 2 years old), low-fat milk, fat-free milk or water is a good beverage choice at meals.

MyPlate Kids' Place has a lot of nutritional resources for parents, caregivers and kids. The online tools and resources are fun, interactive, and help adults and children make healthy food choices. See http://www.choosemyplate.gov/kids/index.html.

How to Bottle-Feed

Babies drink breast milk or formula from a bottle. Toddlers may drink breast milk,

formula, cow's milk, soy milk or water. If the parents want you to give a baby or toddler a bottle, they will probably leave a pre-filled bottle for you in the refrigerator. If they don't plan on leaving a pre-filled bottle for you, make sure they have given you instructions for preparing the bottle. In addition to a bottle filled with the drink of choice, you will need a nipple, a bib and a burp cloth or small towel. Before giving a baby a bottle, always wash your hands.

Although the baby or toddler may prefer a warm bottle, a cold bottle won't hurt him. On the other hand, a bottle that is too warm can burn the baby's or toddler's mouth! If the parents want you to warm the bottle before giving it to the baby or toddler, run it under warm tap water or place it in a bowl of hot tap water (from the faucet) for 30 to 60 seconds. Remember, don't use the microwave to warm a bottle! Gently shake the bottle to distribute the heat, and make sure the liquid inside is heated evenly. Then shake some of the liquid onto the back of your hand to check the temperature. Don't test it on your wrist because your wrist is less sensitive to heat. Also, to avoid the spread of germs, avoid touching the nipple to your skin. The liquid should be lukewarm. If it feels too warm to you, it is too warm for the baby or toddler!

DID YOU KNOW?

Water is the foundation for all body functions! Children need to drink water to be healthy! In general, encourage the child to drink between 6 and 8 cups of water per day. However, if the child is physically active, especially in hot weather, she will require more. Encourage ½ to 2 cups of water every 15 to 20 minutes when the child is physically active!

When you give the baby or toddler the bottle, make sure that his head is higher than his shoulders to help prevent choking. When giving a baby a bottle, hold the bottle at a 45-degree angle to keep air from getting into the nipple. After the baby has taken about one-third of the bottle, burp him and then let him finish the bottle. When the baby is finished, burp him again. If the baby or toddler doesn't finish the bottle, throw away any leftovers. If you put the bottle back in the refrigerator, germs can grow in the leftover liquid and make the child sick if you give him the bottle later.

For step-by-step instructions on giving a baby a bottle, see Skill Sheet 5-6 (Bottle-Feeding) on page 104.

DID YOU KNOW?

Babies younger than 1 year should not be given honey! Honey contains bacteria that can cause muscle weakness and breathing problems in babies.

How to Spoon-Feed

Around the age of 6 months, babies begin eating some solid foods in addition to having their bottles. You will need to spoon-feed solid foods to babies and young toddlers who can't hold a spoon yet.

To spoon-feed a baby or a toddler, you will need an infant or toddler spoon, a dish, the food, a bib, and a clean washcloth for wiping the child's mouth and hands. Wash your hands and the child's hands before beginning. If the parents want you to warm the food before giving it to the child, you can either place the container in a bowl of hot tap water or heat it in the microwave. A typical 4-ounce jar of baby food only needs to be heated in the microwave for about 15 seconds. Stir the food well and then let it stand for 30 seconds. Place a small

amount of food on the back of your hand to test the temperature. The food should be lukewarm. If the food seems too hot, don't blow on it to cool it. Just let it cool by itself. Don't feed the child directly from the jar of baby food and put it back in the refrigerator again. Germs on the spoon can contaminate the remaining food. Instead, put just enough food for one serving on a dish before starting to feed the child.

Put a small amount of food on the tip of the spoon and feed the child. Babies who are just beginning to eat from a spoon may seem to be pushing the food away. Be patient and keep feeding the baby as long as she seems interested. Let toddlers try to feed themselves with the spoon (or their hands, if they want), helping as necessary. It's OK if they make a mess—you can clean them up later!

For step-by-step instructions on spoon-feeding a baby or toddler, see Skill Sheet 5-7 (Spoon-Feeding) on page 106.

How to Serve Meals and Snacks to Older Children

Preschoolers and school-age children can feed themselves, but you will need to prepare their food. Depending on their age and abilities, let them pitch in and help. For example, let a preschooler help put the toppings on her pizza. An older child can help you measure ingredients or set the table. Keep in mind what you learned in Chapter 3 about kitchen safety.

Preschoolers are able to use a spoon and a fork to eat, although many also still like to use their hands. "Finger foods" are a

big hit with this age group! Preschoolers are often picky eaters, and they may not eat much of what they are served. If the child is playing with the food more than eating it, she is probably finished.

Giving Medications

Giving medications to children is a big responsibility! It's very important to talk to the parents in advance about any medical conditions, such as asthma or diabetes, that may require special medications. Also, ask the parents what medications to give if the child is ill or becomes ill while you are caring for the child. If the parents give you permission to give the child medication, have the parents show you exactly what to do. Make sure they write down when to give the medication, how much medication to give and how to give the medication. The parents can use the **Parental Consent and Contact Form** to write down all prescription and over-the-counter (OTC) medication instructions.

You should be aware of the safe practices of medication administration. Before giving the child any medication,

be sure to check the expiration date. If the medication is expired, do not give it! Be sure to check the 5 "Rights" of medication administration before giving the medication:

- The right child. Never give a child a medication prescribed for someone else.

- The right medication. Never give a child a smaller dose of an adult medication formula.

- The right dose. Be sure to use the measuring device that came with the medication to measure and give the dose.

- The right time. Never give a medication early or late; this could lead to giving two doses too close together.

- The right route. Be sure you know how the medication is used. For example, where do the drops go—ears, eyes or nose?

Don't put the medicine in a bottle or sippy cup filled with juice, water, milk or formula. There's no way to tell if the child actually got the dose of medication.

Always wash your hands before administering the medication and after. If you have to apply cream to a child's skin, wear gloves.

If the child spits out the medication or vomits, do not give another dose. Write down what happened and call the parents. If you make a mistake and give the child the wrong medication or too much medication, call the parents and seek medical care if necessary.

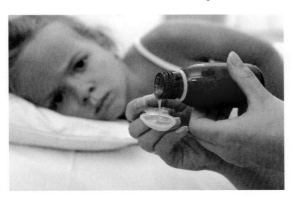

BE SMART, BE SAFE!
Always put medications away and out of reach of the child when you are finished giving the medications.

After you give the child the medication, write down what time you gave the dose and how much you gave. Also, if you couldn't give the dose for any reason, write that down too and call the parents to let them know. Keep a close eye on the child after you give her the medication. If you notice anything unusual (side effects or a reaction), write down what you see and call the parents immediately!

It is a very good idea to keep a medication record with the parents so that everyone sees what medication doses were administered to the child and when. This will help to prevent accidental double dosing or giving the child a second dose too soon after the first one. Discuss what medications you gave to the child (and how much) with the parents when they come home.

BE SMART, BE SAFE! Never give baby aspirin to children! Aspirin use in children during a viral illness can lead to Reye's syndrome, a potentially fatal illness. Never give ibuprofen to infants under 6 months old; acetaminophen is a safe alternative. Also, do not give cold and cough medications to children under 4 years old due to the possibility of serious side effects. In addition, cold and cough medications are not recommended for children 6 years old and under.

Changing Diapers and Helping with the Potty

You may care for children who are still in diapers or who are just learning how to use the potty. When you meet with the parents, have them show you where the diaper-changing supplies are kept and find out what you are supposed to do with the dirty diapers. If the family uses cloth diapers and you aren't used to changing cloth diapers, ask them to show you how.

If the parents have started potty-training their toddler or preschooler, ask whether the child uses a special potty chair or a seat that fits on top of the regular toilet. Some children just use the regular toilet seat. Ask the parents what words or signals the child uses to tell them he needs to use the bathroom. Also find out what the normal routine is, so that you can maintain it. Toilet-training involves giving the child the chance to use the potty chair or toilet at regular times, so you will want to find out what those times are. Some parents may also reward each success with a sticker or another small treat. Remember to take notes on your Family Interview Form!

Changing Diapers

Changing diapers probably won't be your favorite part of the job, but it's a necessary one if you are caring for babies or toddlers. Leaving a child in a dirty diaper is uncomfortable for the child and can cause problems, like skin rashes.

Put the child in a safe place, wash your hands, and check to make sure you have all of the supplies you will need, including baby wipes, a clean diaper, a waste bin for the dirty diaper and your disposable gloves. Here's a tip: make sure your supplies are within your reach, but out of the baby's reach. You might also want to grab a toy for the child to hold while you change the diaper, as well as a washcloth or extra diaper. Sometimes babies will go again when you first unfasten the dirty diaper. You can use the washcloth or extra diaper to cover the baby's front and prevent yourself from getting accidentally sprayed!

When you are ready to change the diaper, put on the gloves and place the child on her back on the changing table or on a water-resistant changing pad on the floor. If you are using a changing table, be sure to fasten the safety straps and keep one hand on the child *at all times* to prevent her from rolling off.

Remove the dirty diaper, set it out of the child's reach and clean the child using the baby wipes. Wipe from front to back and use a clean wipe each time to avoid spreading germs. Be sure to clean in between skin folds. Allow the diaper area to air dry. Exposing a rash to fresh air promotes healing. If the parents instruct you to use a diaper rash cream, use only a thin layer. A thick layer can cake, which can lead to infection. Do not use baby powder. Baby powder can cake and lead to infection, and can also cause respiratory issues in infants.

Put the clean diaper on the child. Throw away the dirty diaper and remove your gloves. If you changed a baby's diaper, wipe the baby's hands with a clean wipe and move her to a safe place before washing your own hands. If you changed a toddler's diaper, you and the toddler can wash your hands together. And that's all there is to it! That doesn't seem so hard, does it?

For step-by-step instructions on diapering, see Skill Sheet 5-8 (Diapering) on page 108.

Helping with the Potty

Some older toddlers and most preschoolers are learning to use the toilet. Wash your hands before and after helping a child use a potty chair or the toilet, and help the child to wash his hands after he is done.

When you are caregiving for a child who is being potty trained, encourage the child to use the potty chair or toilet often. Take him to the bathroom before and after eating, before and after taking a nap, and before and after activities such as playing outside. If the child is showing signs that he has to go to the bathroom, such as clutching at his pants, shivering or jumping around, take him to the bathroom immediately.

When a child who is being potty trained successfully uses the potty chair or toilet, offer lots of praise. But never make a big deal out of an accident! Just clean the child up and say it was a good try. Remember to wear your disposable gloves while you are cleaning the child up and to wash your hands afterwards.

Children who are already toilet-trained sometimes still need help unfastening their clothes, wiping themselves or washing their hands. If you help a girl with wiping, wipe from front to back to keep from spreading germs. Be sure girls who don't need your help know that they should wipe themselves from front to back, too.

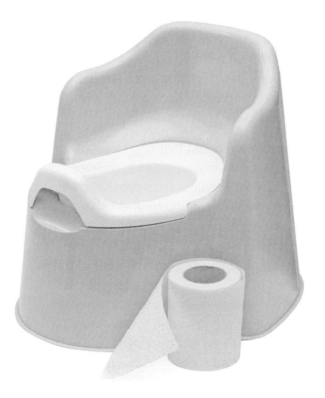

Dressing Children

While you are caring for children, you may have to help them change their clothes. For example, you may have to help a child get into her pajamas before bed, or put an extra layer on over a T-shirt if it's chilly outside and the child is going outside to play.

When you are dressing or undressing a baby, remember to support the baby's head and neck. You can change a baby's clothes on a changing table or on the floor. Remember, never leave a baby alone on a changing table, bed, sofa or any other piece of furniture.

Toddlers are just learning to dress and undress themselves. Undressing is usually easier for toddlers than dressing. Let the toddler help you to undo snaps or buttons, and encourage him to pull off his socks or finish pulling a shirt over his head after you get his arms out of the sleeves. Similarly, let toddlers help to dress themselves as much as they are able. For example, the toddler may be able to pull up her own pants if you get them started for her. Shirts, especially shirts that pull over the head, are usually harder for the toddler to put on and take off. For step-by-step instructions on helping a child put on or take off a shirt, see Skill Sheet 5-9 (Helping a Child Put On and Take Off a Shirt) on page 110. Preschoolers are more skilled at dressing and undressing themselves, but will still need some help from you with tasks like tying shoelaces. When you are helping a toddler or preschooler to change clothes, allow plenty of time and let the child go at his own pace, helping as needed.

Avoid dressing kids in clothes that fasten with drawstrings, especially around the neck. Check to see that the child's clothing fits properly. If pants are too long, roll up the pant legs so that the child doesn't trip. Make sure shoes fit securely and laces are tied. Also make sure that whatever the child is wearing is appropriate for what the child will be doing. For example, if a child is going outside to play, make sure she is wearing brightly colored clothing that is easy to spot. Finally, check for loose buttons or snaps. If these fall off, they can become choking hazards. If you see that a button or snap is loose, set the article of clothing aside and be sure to let the parents know that a repair is needed.

Bathing Children

Bathing young children—especially babies—is a high-risk activity. Only bathe young children if you've specifically been asked to by their parents and you are comfortable giving a child a bath. (See Chapter 3 for safety tips to keep in mind when giving a child a bath.)

Before you run the water, gather all of the supplies and bath toys you will need. When filling the bathtub, turn the hot water on last and off first to help prevent scald burns. You don't have to fill the tub very high. Before letting the child get into the water, move your hand back and forth to test the temperature and make sure there are no hot spots. Never let the child sit in the tub while it is filling!

Help the child into the bathtub because the tub is slippery. Make sure the child stays seated, and keep the child's head away from the faucet. Let the child play a little with her bath toys and get used to the bath before you start washing or shampooing. When shampooing or rinsing the child's hair, tilt her head back to avoid getting water and shampoo in her eyes. Some kids don't like having water on their faces, either. If the child resists having a bath or getting her hair washed, don't force the issue.

When bath time is over, help the child get out of the tub and dry her off. Remember to empty the bathtub as soon as you are finished using it!

Brushing and Flossing a Child's Teeth

If you are caring for a child from morning to evening, parents may give you instructions on brushing and flossing

their child's teeth. Teeth should be brushed twice a day, after breakfast and before bedtime. If you are home with the child after lunch or sweet snacks, it is a good idea to brush at this time as well.

According to the American Academy of Pediatric Dentistry, it is safe to use a smear of fluoride toothpaste when brushing the teeth of children under the age of 2 years old. However, if you are caring for a child this age, the parents may not want you to use fluoride toothpaste when brushing their child's teeth. They will give you instructions on whether to use water only or nonfluorinated baby toothpaste to clean the child's teeth.

You will need to perform or help the child brush her teeth up until she is 6 or 7 years of age. Help the child put a pea-sized amount of toothpaste on her toothbrush. Help her brush all of her teeth (front, back and sides) for at least 2 or 3 minutes. Try singing or playing a recording of a song to help pass the time and to make brushing the teeth fun. Remind the child to spit out the excess toothpaste, and not to swallow it, while brushing. If the parents want you to help the child floss her teeth, help the child slip the dental floss between each tooth and along the gum line gently once a day.

Good Night, Good Morning!

Putting Children to Bed or Down for a Nap

Getting enough sleep and rest is important for kids. Growing up is hard, tiring work! Sleep allows the body to rest and repair itself and get ready for the next adventure.

In addition to sleeping at night, babies and toddlers need naps during the day, too. Many kids continue to take naps right up until the time they start school. When you meet with the family before taking a caregiving job, ask the parents when the child usually takes naps and goes to bed, and what routines the family follows at naptime and bedtime (for example, giving the child a drink or snack before bed, reading a bedtime story, turning on a nightlight, or making sure the child has a special stuffed animal or favorite blanket). You definitely want to know if a child requires a certain teddy bear or a special blankie before bedtime arrives and the teddy bear or blankie is nowhere to be found! Write down when the child needs to go to bed or down for a nap on your Family Interview Form, along with any special instructions relating to bedtime or naptime. Also, if there are baby monitors, ask the parents to show you how to use them.

Even though sleep is important, many kids will resist going to bed or going down for a nap, even if they are very tired. After all, they have a lot to see and do, and they don't want to miss out on any of the fun! Be kind but firm in helping children follow their rest and sleep routines. Tell the child about 15 minutes in advance that bedtime or naptime is approaching, so there are no surprises. Help the child wind down and prepare for sleep by doing a quiet activity with her, like reading a comforting story, listening to soft music or rubbing her back. And of course, always follow the child's normal bedtime or naptime routines. Be sure to have the child use the toilet and brush her teeth before sleeping.

Tell the child to sleep well and say goodnight. Make sure you stay where you can hear the child if she gets up after going to bed for the night or when naptime is over, and check on her every 15 minutes. If a child gets up after going to bed for the night, put her back to bed. You may need to comfort her if she is scared or had a bad dream.

Waking Children Up

Sometimes you will be responsible for waking children up after a nap or in the morning before school. Some children jump right up after a nap or in the morning. Others do not. It is important to wake children calmly and gently from sleep. Put on some soft music, open the drapes and/or turn on the room light to slowly arouse the child from sleep. Lightly touch the child's cheek or rub his or her back, speak softly to the child or sing a song to gently ease the child into wakefulness. Another good idea to get children moving in the morning is to cook a fun and good smelling breakfast to help bring the children to the breakfast table. The smell of

---

Safe Sleep for Babies

When you are taking care of a baby, there are some important things you need to know to keep the baby safe while he is sleeping:

- When it is naptime or bedtime, put the baby in his crib or bassinet to sleep. Chairs, sofas, beds and soft surfaces (such as on a pillow or quilt) are not safe places for babies to sleep.

- Check the crib before putting the baby in it. The crib should contain only a firm mattress covered with a tight-fitting sheet. Don't worry about the baby getting cold without a blanket to cover him—dressing the baby in a sleeper or other sleep clothing is enough to keep him warm without blankets. Remember that blankets, pillows, bumper pads, soft toys and other soft objects in the crib could put the baby at risk of suffocating.

- Babies younger than 1 year should be put to sleep on their backs, face-up, never on their tummies or sides. This is because putting a baby to sleep on his tummy or side increases the baby's risk for sudden infant death syndrome (SIDS). SIDS is the sudden and unexplained death of an otherwise healthy baby while the baby is sleeping. Putting a baby to sleep on his back is one of the most important things you can do to lower the baby's risk for SIDS.

- Make sure the baby's room is a comfortable temperature. Be especially careful that the baby is not too hot when he is sleeping, because being overheated increases the baby's risk for SIDS. The baby may be too hot if he is sweating or if his chest feels hot.

- Check on the sleeping baby frequently.

scrambled eggs or pancakes cooking can be a great morning motivator!

If you have been hired to wake the child and get her to school, there are certain things you can do to help the morning run smoothly. The most important thing to do is to follow the child's morning routine and don't do chores or activities outside of it. Make sure lunches are prepared before the child is awake; make sure the child's backpack is packed and ready; and help the child, as necessary, with dressing, toileting, grooming, eating breakfast and brushing teeth.

Staying Overnight

If you are a live-in caregiver or on an overnight caregiving job, you will be sleeping at the house with the children. Review all of the information provided in Chapter 3 about safety in the home. It is a good idea to keep at least one light on near a window to indicate the house is occupied. Before you go to sleep, check windows from time to time for anything strange outside. Immediately report anything strange that you see to local authorities and to the child's parents.

Always keep the doors to the child's bedroom slightly open so that you will be able to hear the child if she wakes up. Before you go to sleep, check on the child every 15 minutes. If the child wakes up in the middle of the night, comfort her if necessary, help her with any toileting needs and help her get back in bed. She may ask for a drink. A small drink of water is OK, but never give a child juice or milk after she has brushed her teeth.

There are some absolutes when you stay overnight on a job. You should never invite friends or family members over to the house or have a party while you are working. It is also never a good idea to drink alcohol while you are on the job. Always follow the rules set by the parents and never, ever leave the house without the children. Always ask the parents where you should sleep while on the job; be prepared to sleep on the couch if the family does not have a guest room. After the children go to sleep, you should never watch or download inappropriate shows or content on the TV or home computer. Also, don't use the family's phone for personal calls. And, it goes without saying, but don't wake the children up, unless it is an emergency.

Skill Sheet 5-1: Hand Washing

1. If you are wearing long sleeves, push them up so they don't get wet.

2. Turn on the water, and adjust the temperature so that it is warm.

3. Wet your hands under the running water, and apply soap.

4. Rub your hands together to make a lather.

5. Wash your hands for at least 20 seconds (about the time it takes to sing the ABCs). Wash:

   - The palms of your hands.

   - The backs of your hands.

   - In between your fingers.

   - Under your nails (rub the nails of one hand against the palm of the opposite hand).

6. Rinse your hands under the running water.

7. Dry your hands with a paper towel.

8. Use a clean paper towel to turn off the water.

Skill Sheet 5-2: Removing Disposable Gloves

1. Pinch the palm side of one glove near the wrist.

2. Pull the glove toward your fingertips, turning it inside out as you pull it off your hand.

3. Hold the glove in the palm of your gloved other hand.

4. Slip two fingers under the wrist of the other glove.

5. Pull the glove toward your fingertips, turning it inside out as you pull it off your hand. The other glove is now contained inside.

6. Throw away the gloves and wash your hands.

Skill Sheet 5-3: Picking Up an Infant

Note: *Always support the head and neck of a baby younger than 6 months.*

Method 1:

1. Slide both of your hands under the infant's underarms.

2. Wrap your fingers around the infant's ribs.

3. Gently lift the infant.

Method 2:

1. Slide one hand under the infant's head and back.

2. Slide your other hand under the infant's bottom.

3. Gently lift the infant.

Skill Sheet 5-4: Holding an Infant

Note: *Always support the head and neck of an infant younger than 6 months.*

Shoulder Hold:

1. Put one arm under the infant's bottom and the other arm along her back, with your hand supporting her head and neck.

2. Let the infant lean against your chest and look over your shoulder.

Cradle Hold:

1. Support the infant's back along one arm, with her head resting in the crook of your elbow and your hand supporting her bottom.

2. Use your other arm to support the infant's bottom and legs.

Skill Sheet 5-5: Picking Up and Holding a Toddler

1. Bend your knees.

2. Slide both of your hands under the toddler's underarms, wrapping your hands around the toddler's ribs.

3. Stand up, using your legs to lift yourself and the toddler up in a smooth, continuous motion.

4. Put one arm under the toddler's bottom and support her back with your other arm. Hold the toddler in front of you with her legs wrapped around your waist.

Skill Sheet 5-6: Bottle-Feeding

1. Put the child in a safe place.

2. Wash your hands.

3. Gather your supplies. You will need a:

   - Bottle

   - Nipple

   - Bib

   - Burp cloth or small towel

4. Prepare the bottle according to the parents' instructions. If the parents have asked you to warm the bottle:

   - Hold the bottle under warm tap water or place it in a bowl of hot tap water (from the faucet) for 30 to 60 seconds. (Never use the microwave!)

   - Gently shake the bottle to make sure the liquid is heated evenly.

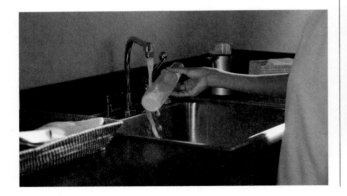

- Test the temperature by shaking a few drops of liquid onto the back of your hand. (To avoid spreading germs, don't touch the nipple to your skin.) The liquid should be lukewarm.

5. Sit down and hold the infant on your lap in a cradle hold, with her head higher than her shoulders. Put the burp cloth over your shoulder.

Continued on next page

Skill Sheet 5-6: Bottle-Feeding *(Continued)*

6. Give the infant the bottle. If the infant cannot hold the bottle by herself, hold it for her. Tilt the bottle to a 45-degree angle so that air does not get into the nipple.

7. When the infant has taken about one third of the bottle, burp her.

- **Method 1:** Hold the infant upright in a shoulder hold. Pat the infant gently on the back until you hear a burp.

- **Method 2:** Sit the infant on your lap and pat her gently on the back until you hear a burp. If the infant is younger than 6 months, make sure to support her head.

8. Reposition the infant comfortably on your lap in the cradle hold, and give her the rest of the bottle.

9. When the infant is finished with the bottle, burp her again.

Skill Sheet 5-7: Spoon-Feeding

1. Put the child in a high chair or infant seat. Buckle the safety strap securely.

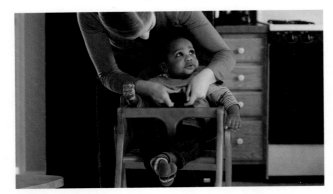

2. Wash your hands and the child's hands.

3. Gather your supplies. You will need:

   - The food

   - An infant or toddler spoon

   - A dish

   - A bib

   - A clean washcloth for wiping the child's hands and mouth

4. Prepare the food according to the parents' instructions. If the parents have asked you to warm the food:

   - Place the container of food in a bowl of hot tap water, or heat it in the microwave. A 4-ounce jar of baby food only needs to be heated in the microwave for about 15 seconds.

   - Stir the food well and then let it stand for 30 seconds.

   - Test the temperature by placing a small amount of food on the back of your hand. To avoid spreading germs, don't touch the spoon to your skin. The food should be lukewarm.

5. Put a small amount of food on the tip of the spoon and feed the child.

Continued on next page

Skill Sheet 5-7: Spoon-Feeding *(Continued)*

6. When you are finished feeding the child, wash his hands and face and wipe up any spilled food.

7. Wash your hands.

Skill Sheet 5-8: Diapering

1. Put the child in a safe place.

2. Wash your hands.

3. Gather your supplies. You will need:

   - A clean diaper

   - Wipes

   - Disposable gloves

   - A waste bin

   - A toy for the child to hold (optional)

   - A clean washcloth or extra diaper for covering the child (optional)

4. Put on your disposable gloves.

5. Place the child on her back on a changing table or on a water-resistant changing pad on the floor. If you are using a changing table:

   - Use the safety straps on the changing table to secure the child.

   - Keep one hand on the child at all times! Never leave a child alone on a changing table.

6. Take off the dirty diaper.

   - Unfasten the sticky tabs. (Now's the time to cover the infant with the washcloth or extra diaper if you are using one!)

   - Use one hand to hold the child's feet and gently lift her bottom up.

   - Slide the dirty diaper out from underneath the child, folding it so that the mess is on the inside.

   - Set the dirty diaper out of the child's reach.

Continued on next page

Skill Sheet 5-8: Diapering *(Continued)*

7. Clean the child with the wipes. Still holding the child's feet and gently lifting her bottom:

   - Wipe from front to back to avoid spreading germs.

   - Use a clean wipe each time to avoid spreading germs.

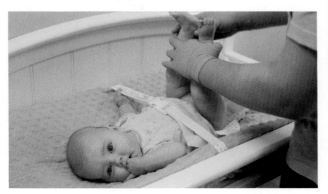

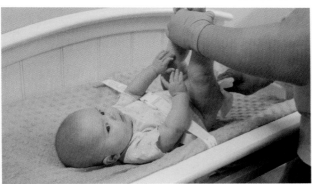

8. Put on the clean diaper.

   - Open the clean diaper and slide it underneath the child. The sticky tabs go in the back and should be about even with the child's belly button.

   - If you are diapering a boy, make sure his penis is pointing down to prevent leaks.

- Bring the front of the diaper between the child's legs, and fasten the sticky tabs. Be sure to stick the tabs to the front of the diaper, not the child's skin.

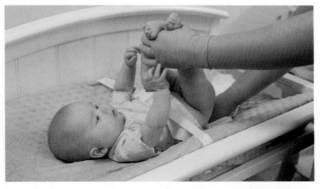

9. Place the dirty diaper and wipes in the disposal bin, and then remove and throw away your gloves.

10. Wipe the child's hands with a clean wipe, and then move her to a safe place.

11. Make sure the changing area is clean. (Put on another pair of disposable gloves if necessary.)

12. Wash your hands.

Skill Sheet 5-9: Helping a Child Put On and Take Off a Shirt

To Put On a Shirt That Pulls Over the Head:

1. Stretch the neck opening of the shirt so that it is larger than the child's head.

2. Put the neck opening over the child's head, keeping the shirt away from the child's ears and face.

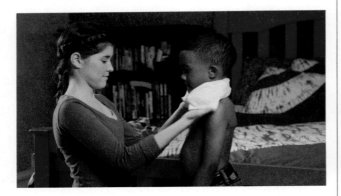

3. Reach through a sleeve opening and gently bring one of the child's arms through it.

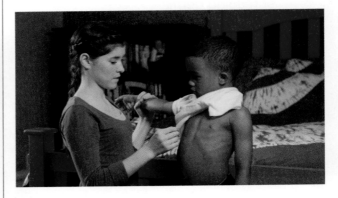

4. Do the same with the other arm.

5. Pull the bottom of the shirt down into place.

To Take Off a Shirt That Pulls Over the Head:

1. Gently slide one arm out of the sleeve, and then slide out the other arm.

2. Lift the shirt over the child's head, gently past one ear and then the other.

Continued on next page

Skill Sheet 5-9: Helping a Child Put On and Take Off a Shirt *(Continued)*

To Put On a Shirt That Fastens in the Front:

1. Open all snaps or buttons.

2. Roll or scrunch up the sleeves if they are long.

3. Reach through one sleeve, grasp the child's hand, and pull the hand and arm gently through the sleeve.

4. Bring the shirt around the back of the child, and help the child put his other arm in the sleeve.

5. Fasten the snaps or buttons.

To Take Off a Shirt that Fastens in the Front:

1. Unfasten all snaps or buttons.

2. Help the child remove one arm from the shirt.

3. Bring the shirt around the child's back and help him to remove the other arm from the shirt.

6 IT'S AN EMERGENCY—NOW WHAT?

Hopefully when you are working, the most eventful thing that will happen is that you will have to change a dirty diaper or cope with a mini-meltdown when someone doesn't want to take a nap. But on the off-chance that a more serious situation occurs while you are working, like a medical emergency or an accident, you need to know how to size up the situation and get help if you need it. Let's take a closer look at how you can prepare for, and respond to, emergencies.

Being Prepared

An emergency is a situation where action is needed right away. As you learned in Chapter 3, there are different kinds of emergencies, such as weather emergencies, fire emergencies, crime-related emergencies and first aid emergencies (that is, emergencies that involve a injury or sudden illness). In this chapter, we're going to focus on being prepared for, and responding to, first aid emergencies.

Overcome Fear and Barriers to Act

When an emergency happens while you are working, it may bring out confusing feelings. You may really want to help the child, but you may also feel scared or unsure of how to handle the situation. These feelings are real and personal! The most common factors that keep people from responding in an emergency and steps you can take to overcoming these barriers are:

- **Panic or fear of doing something wrong.** Knowing what to do in an emergency can instill confidence that can help you to avoid panic and be able to provide the right care. By taking this course, you will know what to do in case of emergency!

- **Being unsure of the child's condition and what to do.** If you are not sure what to do, call 9-1-1 or the local emergency number and follow the instructions of the emergency medical services (EMS) dispatcher or call taker. The worst thing to do is nothing!

- **Assuming someone else will take action.** As the caregiver, you are responsible for the child. Take action and ask for help if there are bystanders.

- **Type of injury or illness.** An injury or illness may be very unpleasant. Blood, vomit, bad odors, deformed body parts, or torn or burned skin can be very upsetting. If necessary, turn away for a moment and take a few deep breaths to get control of your feelings before you give care.

- **Fear of catching a disease.** It is extremely unlikely that you will catch a disease while providing care to the child. However, you should always follow *standard precautions* to prevent germs and disease from spreading when providing care.

- **Fear of being sued.** You may be worried about being sued for giving care. Make sure you have consent from the parents to provide care before an emergency happens. (See next section, Talk to the Parents in Advance.)

- **Being unsure of when to call 9-1-1 or the local emergency number.** While working, always call 9-1-1 or the local emergency number if the child for whom you are caring has a illness or injury!

Stop Germs and Diseases from Spreading

How Germs and Diseases Spread

The most common germs are bacteria and viruses. Bacteria can live outside of the body and do not depend on other organisms for life. The number of bacteria that infect humans is small, but bacteria can cause serious infections. Bacterial infections can be treated with medications. Viruses normally depend on other organisms to live. Once they are in the body, they are difficult to kill and few medications can fight them. Viral infections can range from minor to severe. A person's immune system is the number one protection against infection.

Bacteria and viruses spread from one person to another through direct or indirect contact. Direct contact transmission occurs when germs from the person's blood or other body fluids pass directly into your body through breaks or cuts in your skin or through the lining of your mouth, nose or eyes. Some diseases are transmitted by droplets in the air we breathe. Indirect contact occurs when germs are passed from one person to another through shared objects (for example, spoons, glasses, doorknobs) that have been exposed to the droplets.

How to Prevent Germs and Diseases from Spreading

Follow *standard precautions* whenever you provide First Aid or CPR:

- Be prepared by having a first aid kit handy and stocked with personal protective equipment (PPE), such as disposable gloves, pediatric CPR breathing barriers, eye protection and other supplies.

- Avoid contact with blood and other body fluids or objects that may be soiled with blood and other body fluids.

- Use a pediatric CPR breathing barrier when giving rescue breaths (see Breathing Barriers later in the chapter).

- Use barriers, such as disposable gloves, between the child's blood or body fluids and yourself.

- Do not eat, drink or touch your mouth, nose or eyes when giving care or before you wash your hands after giving care.

- Avoid handling any of your personal items, such as pens or combs, while giving care or before you wash your hands.

- Do not touch objects that may be soiled with blood or other body fluids.

- Wash your hands thoroughly with soap and warm running water when you have finished giving care, even if you wore disposable gloves. Alcohol-based hand sanitizers allow you to clean your hands when soap and water are not readily available and your hands are not visibly soiled. (Keep alcohol-based hand sanitizers out of the reach of children!)

- Tell EMS personnel at the scene or your health care provider if you have come into contact with an injured or ill child's body fluids.

Talk to the Parents in Advance

Before every caregiving job, it's important to find out from the parents how they want you to handle a first aid emergency, such as an allergic reaction, if one occurs while you are watching their kids. Let the parents know what first aid training you have completed, and ask for their consent in advance to provide first aid care for their child if necessary.

Every person has the legal right to decide what can or cannot be done to his or her body. This means that everyone has the legal right to accept or refuse first aid care. When the person who needs care is a child, the child's parents are responsible for making decisions about what care the child receives. This is why it's important to talk to the parents in advance about your level of first aid training, and to ask them if it is OK for you to provide basic first aid care for their child if necessary. Ask them to fill out and sign the **Parental Consent and Contact Form**, which you can download from your online course. You can also check out a sample in Appendix B.

A life-threatening emergency is an emergency situation that could cause permanent injuries or result in the child's death if you don't take immediate action. In a life-threatening emergency:

- If a parent is there when the emergency happens, ask the child's parent if it is OK for you to give care.

- If a parent is not there and you haven't received permission in advance to give care, you should still give care according to your level of training. In this type of situation, permission is

implied. You can assume that if the parent were there, he or she would tell you it is OK to give care to the child. If you have not received the parents' permission in advance to give care or you are unsure of what to do, you can always call 9-1-1 or the local emergency number. Then be sure to call the parents.

It's also important to talk to the parents in advance about any medical conditions the child may have, such as asthma, diabetes or allergies. Ask the parents if there are special instructions you should follow when caring for their child. For example, if the parents want you to give the child medication, have the parents show you exactly what to do, and make sure they write down when to give the medication and how much medication to give. The parents can use the Parental Consent and Contact Form to write down all special instructions relating to the child's medical care.

BE SMART, BE SAFE! If you are unsure of what to do, you can always call 9-1-1 or the local emergency number. Then be sure to call the parents.

Finally, make sure the parents leave you information that will be important to know in case you need to call for help. The **Family Emergency Information Card**, which you can download from your online course, is an easy way to collect key information, such as:

- The phone number where the parents can be reached.

- The phone number to call in the event of an emergency (if not 9-1-1).

- Other phone numbers that you might need in an emergency, such as that of the child's doctor, other family members and the poison control center.

- The home's address and the name of the nearest cross street (this information helps emergency responders find you quickly).

Have a First Aid Kit Ready

A first aid kit contains items that are useful if a first aid emergency arises. You can make your own kit or buy a kit. If you do not have a first aid kit, ask the parents to show you where they keep their family first aid kit when you meet with them before the job. Also ask them if you can look inside to make sure it has all of the supplies you might need.

Before going on any caregiving job, make sure your first aid kit is well stocked and ready to use. It's a good idea to put the completed Family Emergency Information Card in your first aid kit too. When you're on the job, keep your first aid kit handy but out of reach of the kids. (Some of the things that are typically kept in a first aid kit, like scissors, disposable gloves and hand sanitizer, can be dangerous if a child plays with them.) If you and the kids go out (for example, to the park or playground), take your first aid kit with you.

First Aid and CPR Certification

By reading this handbook and taking this course, you're taking a big step toward being a well-prepared caregiver. The best-prepared caregivers are those who are trained in basic first aid and cardiopulmonary resuscitation (CPR) in addition to all of the other important

DID YOU KNOW?

One very important principle of giving first aid is "Do no further harm." Formal training in first aid and CPR gives you the knowledge and skills you need to give the right emergency care.

things you've read about so far. CPR is a lifesaving first aid skill that is done when a person's heart or breathing has stopped. You will read more about basic first aid and CPR in Chapters 7 and 8 of this book, and you will receive certification in Pediatric First Aid and CPR after completing this American Red Cross Advanced Child Care Training course!

Putting Together a First Aid Kit

Before every caregiving job, put the completed Family Emergency Information Card in your first aid kit. **Then make sure your kit contains the following:**

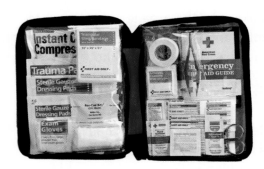

- Nitrile gloves (nonlatex, nonvinyl; 2 pairs)

- Supplies to control bleeding: sterile or nonsterile gauze pads, 4 x 4 inches or 2 x 2 inches (8)

- Supplies to secure dressing: roller bandage, 2 inches, 3 inches or 4 inches x 4 yards (4)

- Adhesive tape, ⅜ inch x 2 yards

- Triangular bandages (3 or 4)

- Latex-free Band-Aids or nonadhesive bandage alternatives (3 each):

  ○ 1 x 3 inches

  ○ ¾ x 3 inches

  ○ large fingertip

  ○ knuckle

- Wound gel ointment

- Compact, moldable splinting device

- Plastic bag (1 quart and/or 1 gallon size) for application of crushed ice (4) and/or instant cold packs (2)

- Irrigation solution (optional)

- Baby aspirin, 81 mg (4)

- Oral glucose tablet, 20 mg (2)

- Utility shears/scissors

- Alcohol-based hand sanitizer

- Splinter forceps/tweezers

- Latex-free face shield

- First aid guide book or *Advanced Child Care Training Handbook*

You can also include:

- A notepad

- A pen or pencil

- A small battery-powered flashlight

- Safety scissors

Responding to First Aid Emergencies

If a first aid emergency occurs, stay calm and follow three basic emergency action steps: **CHECK–CALL–CARE**.

Check

The very first thing you should do in an emergency situation is check the scene. Make sure the area is safe for you to enter and look for clues as to what might have happened. Then, check the child.

Check the scene

Before rushing to help a child who is injured or ill, first make sure there is nothing in the area that could hurt you too. Use your senses. Do you see anything potentially dangerous, like fire or downed electrical lines? Do you smell something that could signal danger, like gas, smoke or chemicals? Is there anything in the area that could hurt you, like a dog or an unstable object? If so, you need to stay at a safe distance and call 9-1-1 or the local emergency number immediately, in order to get additional help from a trained rescuer.

Check the child

After you check the scene, you need to check the child to see what is wrong. First, check to see if the child is conscious. The child is conscious if she is crying or talking, trying to move, or able to look at you or answer you when you speak to her. If the child is not making any noise and not moving, then she may be unconscious. To see if a child is

In an Emergency

CHECK   CALL   CARE

unconscious, tap her shoulder (if she is older than 1 year) or the bottom of her foot (if she is younger than 1 year) and ask her in a loud voice if she is OK. If the child is simply sleeping, the sound of your voice and the tapping should

DID YOU KNOW?

During the family interview, ask the parents if their child wears a medical alert bracelet or necklace for a known medical condition. When checking the child, take note of any medical alert jewelry.

cause a reaction, such as crying or movement. If there is no response, then the child is unconscious.

Checking a conscious child

Begin by getting down at eye level with the child. Reassure the child that you are going to help him. Look the child over and notice if he seems alert, or confused or sleepy. Check out the child's skin—does it appear to be its normal color, or does it seem pale or flushed (red)? Also look for changes from how the child normally acts. This is especially important when you are checking an infant or a young toddler who does not have the words yet to tell you what is wrong. For example, a toddler with a hurt arm may rub the spot that hurts or try to move the arm as little as possible. An infant who is in pain may seem very stiff or tense, arch his back or squeeze his eyes tightly shut. An older sibling might also help you determine if the child is behaving unusually. If you are checking an older child, ask questions about what happened in a way that the child can easily answer. Using simple words, ask the child if she hurts anywhere and if she is having any trouble breathing. Note if the child has pain or discomfort or is unable to move a body part at all.

Next, begin to check the child from toe to head. Checking in this order gives the child a chance to get used to the process and allows her to see what is going on. As you check each part of the

body, look for bleeding, cuts, bruising or swelling. Do not move any areas where there is pain or discomfort, or if you suspect a head, neck or spinal injury. If the child is old enough to respond to your requests, ask her to wiggle her toes and feet and bend her knees, one at a time, if she does not report any pain or altered sensations. Note whether the child is able to move normally, or if she experiences pain or discomfort while moving. Repeat this process with the child's arms, and then check the child's stomach and chest, shoulders, neck and head. For step-by-step instructions on checking a conscious child, see Skill Sheet 6-1 (Checking a Conscious Child) on page 131.

If the child can move without pain and there are no other signs of injury, have him rest in a sitting or other comfortable position. When the child feels ready, help him stand up slowly. If your check reveals a minor injury or you suspect an injury or illness, provide care according to your level of training and call the parents to let them know what is going on. Be alert to signals that the child's condition is worsening, such as faster or slower breathing, changes in skin color and restlessness. These could be signals of shock, a life-threatening condition. If the injury or illness seems severe or if the child's condition is worsening, call 9-1-1 or the local emergency number and provide care according to your level of training until help arrives.

Head, Neck or Spinal Injuries

Head, neck and spinal injuries can be very serious. If you think a child might have a head, neck or spinal injury, it's important to avoid unnecessary movement. Moving the child's head, neck or spinal may cause additional injuries that may be permanent, like paralysis.

You should consider the possibility of a head, neck or spinal injury if the child:

- Was hit by a car, thrown from a moving car, or was in a car accident and was not properly secured in a child safety seat.

- Is wearing a safety helmet that is broken.

- Was injured as a result of a fall from a height greater than his own height.

- Says he has neck or back pain.

- Says his arms or legs feel "tingly" or weak.

- Is not fully alert.

- Staggers when trying to walk.

- Appears to be weak.

If you suspect a head, neck or spinal injury, first call 9-1-1 or the local emergency number. Then:

- If the child is conscious, place your hands on both sides of the child's head, keeping it in the position you found it. If the child's head is sharply turned to the side, do not move it. Just support it in that position.

- If the child is unconscious, follow the steps for checking an unconscious child. You'll learn more about how to check an unconscious child later in this chapter.

Checking an unconscious child

Loss of consciousness could be a sign of a life-threatening problem. For example, problems with the heart or with breathing can cause a person to lose consciousness. If you discover that a child is unconscious, have someone call 9-1-1 or the local emergency number, and then check the child and give care according to the conditions that you find and your level of training. If you are alone, check the child and then call 9-1-1 or the local emergency number based on the conditions you find. To check an unconscious child, remember your ABCs—airway, breathing and circulation.

Airway

The airway, or windpipe, allows air to enter and leave the lungs. When a child is unconscious and lying on his back, the tongue can fall toward the back of the throat, blocking the airway and preventing the child from breathing. You need to "open the airway" so you can check to see if the child is breathing, and also to keep the tongue from blocking the throat.

A technique called the head-tilt/chin-lift maneuver is used to open the airway in a child or infant who does not have a suspected injury to the head,

Understanding Kids of All Ages: Communicating with Children

Infant (Newborn to 12 months) 	■ Infants are unable to communicate with words when they are hurt or uncomfortable. However, they do communicate through crying and other nonverbal cues, such as clenching their fists and arching their backs. ■ When communicating with infants, pay close attention to their nonverbal cues. ■ Use a soothing, "sing-song" tone when speaking with infants. ■ Touch or cuddle with infants to reassure and comfort them.
Toddler (1 to 3 years old) 	■ Toddlers communicate with short, 2- or 3-word sentences. They use assertive words (for example, "no" and "mine") and action words (for example, "hurt finger"). ■ Toddlers also communicate through gestures and tone of voice. ■ When speaking with toddlers, use short sentences and simple words. Use a gentle tone. Pay close attention to their nonverbal cues. ■ Use gestures, pictures and stuffed animals or dolls to assist with communication. For example, ask the child to tell a favorite doll how she is feeling. ■ Give toddlers a choice whenever possible. ■ Touch or cuddle with toddlers to reassure and comfort them.
Preschooler (3 to 4 years old) 	■ Preschoolers begin to use more complicated words. They communicate their ideas more effectively than toddlers, but they may have difficulty with certain concepts. ■ Preschoolers like to imitate other people's words. "No" and "why" are favorite words. ■ Preschoolers begin to understand the concept of cause and effect, but use magical thinking to make fantastic connections. For example, a preschool child might feel that he got sick because he lost his blanket. This can cause fears that may seem irrational to you. ■ The sight of blood may be disturbing to preschoolers, but a dressing or bandage can usually calm the situation ■ Give preschoolers your full attention, using a gentle tone when speaking. ■ Help them put their feelings into words, but clue into their nonverbal cues. ■ Validate preschoolers' emotions and reassure them when they are fearful or anxious. Appealing to their imagination might help calm them in stressful situations. ■ Use play and art to assist with communication. Ask the child to draw a picture to express how he is feeling. ■ Help preschoolers figure out their problem and involve them in the solution. Give them choices whenever possible.

School-Age Child	
(5 to 10 years old) 	■ School-age children think more logically and understand complex concepts. They also have a more sophisticated sense of humor.
	■ School-age children can tailor their communication styles to different situations and might be more private with their thoughts.
	■ School-age children begin to question, doubt or criticize parents and other adults.
	■ School-age children are often fascinated by the concept of death and may have strong fantasies or imaginary ideas, such as thinking they can protect themselves by avoiding stepping on cracks in the sidewalk.
	■ Speak with school-age children in a mature and respectful fashion.
	■ Ask specific rather than general questions.
	■ Actively listen to school-age children without judgment.
	■ Use reflective statements to repeat back what they have said.
	■ Use humor when appropriate.
	■ Provide continual reassurance during any sort of emergency.

neck or spine. To do a head-tilt/chin-lift maneuver, place one of your hands on the child's forehead, and two fingers of your other hand on the bony part of the child's chin. Tilt the head back. For a child older than 1 year, tilt the head so that the chin is slightly further back from straight up and down. For a infant, tilt the head so that the

chin is straight up and down (parallel with the floor or ceiling). If you think that the child or infant has a head, neck or spinal injury, carefully tilt the head and lift the chin just enough to open the airway.

Breathing

Next, check for breathing. Lean close to the child's face and tilt your head so that you can *look* to see if the child's chest is rising and falling, *listen* for the sounds of breathing and *feel* the child's breath against your cheek. Normal breathing is quiet and regular, and both sides of the chest rise and fall evenly. Occasional or irregular gasps are *not* normal breathing. Spend only about 10 seconds checking for breathing.

If the child is not breathing, you will either continue your check by giving 2 "rescue breaths" or you will begin

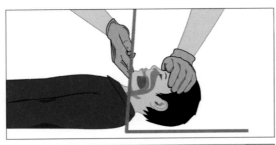

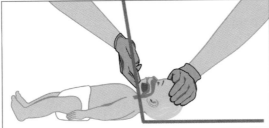

Shock

I'm in shock! We use this expression a lot to mean we are surprised or upset by something, but "shock" is a real medical condition too. In fact, it's life threatening. Shock occurs when the heart and blood vessels are not able to supply all parts of the body with enough blood. As a result, body systems and organs begin to fail. Common causes of shock include severe bleeding and severe allergic reactions (anaphylaxis), but shock can develop after any serious injury or illness.

Signals that a child may be going into shock include:

- Restlessness or irritability.
- Altered level of consciousness.
- Nausea or vomiting.

- Pale, ashen or grayish, cool, moist skin.
- Rapid breathing and pulse.
- Excessive thirst.

A child showing signals of shock needs immediate medical attention. Send someone to call 9-1-1 or the local emergency number. Have the child lie down. If the child is bleeding, control the bleeding. Keep the child from becoming chilled or overheated. Even though the child may say she is thirsty, don't give her anything to drink (or to eat). Comfort and reassure the child until help arrives.

CPR. Rescue breaths get oxygen into the child's body and may cause the child to start breathing on his own again if the child is having a breathing emergency. Give rescue breaths if you did not actually see the child collapse and lose consciousness. But if you actually saw the child collapse and lose consciousness, don't worry about giving rescue breaths now. Instead, begin

CPR right away. This is because sudden collapse is a sign that the child is having a problem with his heart rather than his breathing, and in this case the sooner you begin CPR, the better.

For step-by-step instructions on checking an unconscious child, including giving rescue breaths, see Skill Sheet 6-2 (Checking an Unconscious Child) on page 133.

Circulation

Circulation refers to the movement of blood throughout the body. If the child is bleeding heavily, then he may be having problems with circulation that could lead to a loss of consciousness. Quickly scan the child's body for severe bleeding.

Breathing Barriers

You may feel uncomfortable putting your mouth on someone else's to give rescue breaths. While it's normal to worry about this, the chance of getting a disease from giving rescue breaths is very low. Using a breathing barrier can lower that risk even more.

A breathing barrier is a piece of equipment that you place over the person's mouth and nose while giving rescue breaths. The barrier protects you from coming into contact with the person's body fluids.

There are several types of breathing barriers, including face shields and resuscitation masks. The most basic and portable type of breathing barrier is a face shield, which is small enough to be carried in a pouch on a key ring. The face shield is a flat piece of thin plastic that you place over the child's face, with the opening over the child's mouth (or mouth and nose if you are giving rescue breaths to an infant). The opening contains a filter or a valve that protects you from coming into contact with the child's body fluids.

Keep a breathing barrier in your first aid kit and on your key ring, and make sure you know how to use it. You can buy breathing barriers online at redcross.org.

Call

If a child is seriously injured or has a serious illness, you are going to need to get help from emergency responders, people who are trained to give emergency medical care. Most people in the United States call 9-1-1 for help in first aid emergencies (as well as in fire emergencies and crime-related emergencies). Examples of first aid emergencies that require a call to 9-1-1 include loss of consciousness, trouble breathing and severe bleeding.

If someone is with you, such as a child old enough to use the telephone, have the child call 9-1-1 or the local emergency number while you give care. Otherwise, make the call yourself. When you call 9-1-1 or the local emergency number, the person who answers the phone (called the dispatcher)

will ask you questions to get a better understanding of what is going on, where you are and what kind of help to send. Be prepared to tell the dispatcher:

- What type of emergency you are having (for example, a first aid emergency, a fire, an intruder in the house).

- Who you are.

- Where you are (the street address and the name of the nearest cross street).

- What phone number you are calling from.

- What happened.

- How many people are hurt.

- What type of care, if any, is being given.

Emergency Responders

Emergency responders are the people who help when there is an emergency. Often the first emergency responder who will help you is the dispatcher (call taker). Other emergency responders include:

- Paramedics, who are trained to give advanced-level medical care at the scene of an emergency.

- Emergency medical technicians (EMTs), who are trained to give basic-level medical care at the scene of an emergency.

- Police officers, firefighters and other professional rescuers (for example, ski patrollers, park rangers).

Then, stay on the phone until the dispatcher tells you it is OK to hang up. The dispatcher may need more information from you. Sometimes, the dispatcher will stay on the phone with you and walk you through what to do until help arrives. If the dispatcher tells you it is OK to hang up, return to the child and give care until help arrives. An ambulance may arrive first, or police or firefighters may come to help if they can get there first. After help arrives, call the child's parents and tell them what happened.

In most cases, you will call for help (or have someone else call for help) and then start giving care. But there are two exceptions to that rule!

DID YOU KNOW?

In some areas of the United States, you may need to dial a local emergency number instead of 9-1-1. If you live or work in an area where 9-1-1 is *not* the number you should call in an emergency, find out what the local emergency number is.

DID YOU KNOW?

Phone carriers are required to connect 9-1-1 calls made from a mobile phone, even if the phone does not have an active service plan. Also, you cannot text 9-1-1 from a mobile phone. You must call!

DID YOU KNOW?

If the child you are watching accidentally calls 9-1-1, they will call back or send someone to investigate.

child suddenly collapse, then you should call first because in this case, the child is probably having a heart emergency.

If you are alone and the child has been pulled from the water following a near-drowning accident, then you need to give 2 minutes of care before calling for help. This is because near-drowning is also a breathing emergency.

Care

The care you give depends on the kind of emergency. In Chapter 7, you will learn the skill of CPR and how to

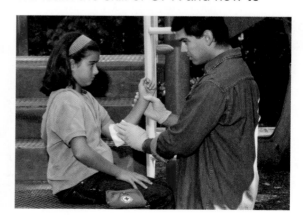

If you are alone, the child is unconscious and you did not see the child collapse, then you need to give 2 minutes of care (CPR) before calling for help. This is because when a child is unconscious but you did not see the child collapse, the child is more likely to be having a breathing emergency than a heart emergency. In a breathing emergency, the priority is getting oxygen into the child's body, but in a heart emergency, the priority is getting help on the scene as soon as possible. If you know that the child has heart problems, or if you see the

Recovery Positions

Recovery positions are positions that are used to help keep an unconscious person's airway open so that he can breathe. Recovery positions are used when you must leave an unconscious person alone (for example, to call for help). Recovery positions are also used if the person's airway might become blocked (for example, because he starts to vomit).

If a child is unconscious but breathing normally and you are sure there are no head, neck or spinal injuries, position the child so that he is lying on his back, facing up. Stay with the child and make sure he continues to breathe normally. If you need to leave the child for any reason, place him in a recovery position.

To place the child in a recovery position, kneel at the child's side and extend the arm farthest from you up. Bend the child's knees, and roll him away from you onto his side while supporting his head and neck. Rest the child's head on his extended arm, and make sure both knees remain bent. Position the child's other arm so that it is straight and resting along the top of his body.

If you must leave the child to get help, position this arm so that the hand is in the armpit of the extended arm, with the palm down and the fingers under the child's chin.

To place an infant in a recovery position, position her face-down along your forearm, supporting her head and neck while keeping her mouth and nose clear.

This position allows you to take the infant with you when you go to call for help or answer the door when help arrives.

properly give care in breathing and heart emergencies. In Chapter 8, you will learn about the care for some common first aid emergencies that may happen while you are working. You can also look up the first aid steps for specific emergencies in Appendix D (First Aid Emergencies from A to Z) at the end of this book.

Call First

if **12+** The victim is about 12 years or older and is unconscious. **OR** **!** The victim is a child or infant whom you saw collapse. **OR** You are caring for a child or infant with a heart condition.

Care First

if **12 and under** The victim is a child or infant whom you did not see collapse. **OR** You are caring for a drowning victim of any age.

To Move or Not to Move?

In most cases, you should *not* move an injured or ill child. Moving a child who is injured can cause additional injury and pain, so only move a child with serious injuries if it is absolutely necessary. Move a child who is seriously hurt only in the following three situations:

- When you are faced with immediate danger, such as the risk of a fire starting or an explosion in the area (but only if you can move the child without putting yourself in danger too).

- When you have to get to another person who may have a more serious injury or illness.

- When you need to move the child to give proper care.

If you must move the child for one of these reasons, you need to quickly decide how to move him. There are many ways to move an injured child. Some work better in certain situations than others. The table on pages 129 to 130 shows different ways you can move an injured child.

When you must move an injured child, you need to consider the child's safety as well as your own. For example, if you think that the child may have a head, neck or spinal injury, then it's very important to avoid twisting or bending the child's head, neck or spine. To avoid injuring yourself when moving a child, bend at your knees and hips (not your waist) and avoid twisting your body. Walk forward when possible, taking small steps and looking where you are going.

Emergency Moves

Move	When to Use It	How to Do It
Walking Assist	To move a child who can walk but needs help	1. Place the child's arm around your shoulder or waist (depending on how tall the child is), and hold it in place with one hand. 2. Support the child with your other hand around the child's waist.(Another person can also support the child in the same way on the other side.)
Pack-Strap Carry	To move a conscious or unconscious child	1. Stand in front of the child, with your back to the child's front. 2. Place the child's arms over your shoulders and cross them in front of your neck. Grasp the child's wrists. 3. Kneeling close to the ground if you have to, lean forward slightly and pull the child onto your back. Use the power in your legs to lift yourself and the child up.
Two-Person Seat Carry	To move a conscious child	1. Put one arm under the child's thighs and the other across his back, under his arms. Have the person who is helping you do the same. 2. Interlock your arms with the other person's arms under the child's legs and across the child's back. 3. Lift the child in the "seat" formed by your interlocked arms.

Move	When to Use It	How to Do It
Clothes Drag 	To move a conscious or unconscious child who may have a head, neck or spinal injury	1. Grasp the child's shirt behind the neck, gathering enough material so that you have a firm grip. 2. Cradle the child's head with his shirt and your hands and pull the child to safety.
Blanket Drag 	To move a conscious or unconscious child	1. Fold the blanket in half lengthwise, and place it so that the fold is alongside the child's body. 2. Take the top layer of the folded blanket and roll it toward the child's body. 3. Position yourself so that the child is between you and the blanket. 4. Put one hand on the child's shoulder and the other on his hip and roll the child onto his side, toward you, and then pull the blanket toward you so that it is against the child's body. 5. Roll the child onto his back, onto the blanket. 6. Pull the side of the blanket that was rolled up toward yourself, so that the child is in the middle of the blanket. 7. Gather the blanket at the child's head and pull the child to safety.
Ankle Drag 	To move a child who is too large to move another way	1. Firmly grasp the child's ankles. 2. Move backwards, pulling the child in a straight line and being careful not to bump his head.

Skill Sheet 6-1: Checking a Conscious Child

1. Get down at eye level with the child and reassure the child that you are going to help him.

2. Look the child over and note any changes from how the child normally looks or acts.

   - Does the child look alert, or does she seem confused, sleepy or "out of it"?

   - How does her skin look and feel? Does the child's skin seem pale or flushed (red)? Does her skin feel cool, hot or sweaty?

   - Is the child showing signals of pain?

   - Does the child seem to be having trouble breathing?

3. If the child is old enough to answer your questions, ask:

   - What happened?

   - Are you having any trouble breathing?

   - Does anything hurt?

   - Where are you hurt?

4. Check the child toe to head. As you check each part of the body, look for bleeding, cuts, bruising or swelling. Note if the child has pain or discomfort or is unable to move the body part at all.

   Note: *Do not ask the child to move any areas that hurt or cause additional pain. Do not ask the child to move at all if you think there is an injury to the head, neck or spine.*

- **Feet and legs.** Ask the child to wiggle his toes and feet and bend his knees, one at a time.

- **Hands and arms.** Ask the child to wiggle his fingers and hands and bend his elbows, one at a time.

- **Stomach and chest.** Ask the child to take a deep breath and blow the air out.

Continued on next page

Skill Sheet 6-1: Checking a Conscious Child

(Continued)

- **Shoulders.** Ask the child to shrug his shoulders.

- **Head and neck.** Ask the child to move his head from side to side. Check the child's scalp, face, ears, eyes, nose and mouth for cuts, bumps, bruises or other signals of injury.

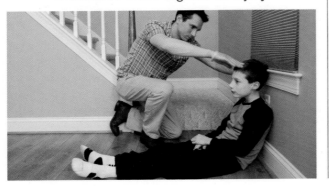

5. Give care according to the conditions that you find. Call 9-1-1 or the local emergency number for any life-threatening conditions.

Skill Sheet 6-2: Checking an Unconscious Child

1. Make sure that the child is unconscious.

   For a child older than 1 year: Tap the child's shoulder and shout, "Are you OK?"

   For an infant: Tap the bottom of the infant's foot and shout, "Are you OK?"

2. Open the airway. Place one hand on the forehead and two fingers on the bony part of the chin and tilt the head back.

   For a child older than 1 year: Tilt the head back until the chin is slightly further back than straight up and down.

For an infant: Tilt the head back until the chin is straight up and down (parallel with the floor or ceiling).

For a suspected a head, neck or spinal injury: Carefully tilt the head and lift the chin just enough to open the airway.

3. Check for breathing. Look, listen and feel for normal breathing for no more than 10 seconds.

   ■ If the child is breathing normally, make sure 9-1-1 or the local emergency number has been called (or, if you are alone, put the child in the recovery position and call the emergency number yourself). Then give care according to the conditions you find until help arrives.

   ■ If the child is not breathing normally and you did not see the child suddenly collapse, give 2 rescue breaths (step 4). Make sure 9-1-1 or the local emergency number has been called, and give care according to the conditions you find until help arrives. If you are alone, give 2 minutes of care before putting the child in the recovery position and calling 9-1-1 or the local emergency number yourself.

Continued on next page

■ If the child is not breathing normally and you saw the child suddenly collapse, make sure 9-1-1 or the local emergency number has been called (or make the call yourself) and then begin CPR immediately.

4. Give rescue breaths if the child is not breathing normally and you did not see the child suddenly collapse.

For a child older than 1 year:

■ Place a breathing barrier, if you have one, over the child's nose and mouth.

■ With the airway open (that is, the head tilted back and the chin lifted), use your hand on the child's forehead to pinch the nose shut.

■ Make a complete seal over the child's mouth with your mouth. Breath into the child's mouth for about 1 second, then let the air out by releasing the seal.

■ If the chest does not rise with the first rescue breath, retilt the head and attempt another rescue breath.

■ If the chest does not rise with the second rescue breath, the airway is blocked. You will need to give care for an unconscious choking child.

For an infant:

■ Place a breathing barrier, if you have one, over the infant's nose and mouth.

■ With the airway open (that is, the head tilted back and the chin lifted), make a complete seal over the infant's mouth and nose with your mouth. Breathe into the infant's mouth for about 1 second, then let the air out by releasing the seal.

■ If the chest does not rise with the first rescue breath, retilt the head and attempt another rescue breath.

■ If the chest does not rise with the second rescue breath, the airway is blocked. You will need to give care for an unconscious choking infant.

5. Quickly scan for severe bleeding.

6. Give care according to the conditions that you find.

CPR/AED–
LIFESAVING SKILLS

f all you know about CPR and AED is what you've seen on television or in the movies, then you probably know they can save lives. But have you ever learned how to give CPR or how to use an AED? Let's take a closer look at these skills that everyone should know.

Background

CPR is short for cardiopulmonary resuscitation. *Cardio* mean "heart." *Pulmonary* means "lungs." And *resuscitation* means "to bring back to life." You probably remember from health class that every organ in the body needs a steady supply of oxygen in order to work properly. The lungs bring oxygen into the body, and the heart moves oxygen-rich blood throughout the body. If the heart stops beating (a condition called *cardiac arrest*), it is unable to do its job of moving the blood. CPR is a skill that is used in cardiac arrest to keep oxygen-rich blood moving throughout the body until medical help arrives.

Usually when we think of giving CPR, we think of giving first aid to a person who has had a heart attack. A heart attack is certainly one reason why a person's heart would stop beating, and it is the most common reason in adults. However, kids don't usually have heart attacks. In kids, it's much more common for a breathing emergency (like drowning, suffocation or choking) to cause the heart to stop beating. If the body's supply of oxygen is interrupted, the heart soon stops beating. (Remember, *every* organ in the body needs a steady supply of oxygen in order to work properly, and the heart is no exception!)

Sometimes, though, the cause of cardiac arrest in kids is related to a problem with the heart itself. For example, some kids have congenital heart conditions (that is, a heart disorder they were born with). Severe injuries that affect the heart, such as those that might be caused by getting struck by a car, being struck hard in the chest or being electrocuted or struck by lightening, can also cause the heart to stop beating. In cardiac emergencies like these, CPR alone is not enough to help the child survive cardiac arrest. An AED (which is short for *automated external defibrillator*) and emergency medical care are needed as soon as possible!

Cardiac Emergencies

When the problem is with the heart itself, the child's greatest chance of surviving occurs when you follow the four steps below. These four steps are called the Cardiac Chain of Survival. Each step must happen one after the other as rapidly as possible:

1. **Early recognition and early access to emergency medical services (EMS).** If you know that an unconscious child has heart problems, or if you see the child suddenly collapse (for example, after being struck in the chest with a line drive ball), chances are the child is having a cardiac emergency. In a cardiac emergency, the priority is getting help on the scene as quickly as possible. The sooner 9-1-1 or the local emergency number is called, the sooner medical help will arrive.

Cardiac Chain of Survival

Early Recognition   **Early CPR**   **Early Defibrillation**   **Early Advanced Medical Care**

2. **Early CPR.** CPR helps move oxygen-containing blood throughout the body and to vital organs, such as the brain.

3. **Early defibrillation.** An AED is a machine that can analyze the heart's rhythm and give an electrical shock that may help to get the heart pumping normally again.

4. **Early advanced medical care.** Emergency responders are trained to give more advanced medical care, increasing the child's chances for survival.

You are the first link in the Cardiac Chain of Survival! It is important to recognize what is happening, call 9-1-1 or the local emergency number and begin CPR quickly. Continue giving CPR until an AED is available or emergency responders arrive and take over. A delay in any part of the chain makes it less likely that the child will survive.

CPR

If you check an unconscious child and find that he is not breathing normally, you will need to give CPR. CPR involves giving sets of 30 chest compressions followed by 2 rescue breaths.

When you give compressions, you press down on the child's chest. This squeezes (or "compresses") the heart, moving blood out of it and through the body. After each compression, you must let the chest return to its normal resting position. This allows blood to flow into the heart again. The rescue breaths you give after each set of 30 compressions deliver a fresh supply of oxygen into the child's lungs. When you give CPR, you help to keep oxygen-rich blood moving throughout the body, which can buy the child some time until more advanced medical help arrives.

Giving CPR to a child older than 1 year

Doing compressions and rescue breaths the right way is important. First, you want to make sure the child is lying face-up on a firm, flat surface. (You need something to push against!) Kneel beside the child. Place the heel of one hand in the center of his chest, with your other hand on top. If you can feel the notch at the end of the child's breastbone, move your hands up a little bit, toward his head. Lean forward so that your shoulders are directly over your hands. This will let you push on the chest using a straight up-and-down motion, which lets you move the most blood with each push and is also less tiring. Keeping your arms straight, push down about 2 inches and then let the chest return to its normal resting position. Don't take your hands off the child's chest—just your weight. Push hard and push fast! You want to try to go at a rate of 100 compressions per minute. (If you're into music, that's the same as a song with a tempo of 100 BPM, or beats per minute.)

After you give 30 compressions, you stop and give 2 rescue breaths. Place the breathing barrier over the child's nose and mouth. Make sure the child's airway is open by keeping the head tilted back. Pinch the nose shut and make a complete seal over the child's mouth with your mouth. Take a normal breath and blow in just enough to make the child's chest clearly rise. The breath should last about 1 second. Pause, release the seal and let the air out before giving the second rescue breath. (Remember, if the first rescue breath doesn't make the chest clearly rise, retilt the head before giving the second rescue breath.) After you have given 2 rescue breaths, remove the breathing barrier and start another set of 30 chest compressions.

Once you begin CPR, don't stop. Keep going until:

- You see an obvious sign of life, such as breathing.

- An AED is available and ready to use.

- Another trained rescuer (such as an emergency responder) takes over.

- You are too tired to continue.

- The scene becomes unsafe.

When you are giving CPR, the child may vomit. If this happens, roll the child onto one side and wipe his mouth clean. (Hopefully, you are wearing your disposable gloves, but if not, try to use something like a tissue or a piece of gauze to wipe out the mouth.) Then roll the child onto his back again and continue giving care.

For step-by-step instructions on giving CPR to a child older than 1 year, see Skill Sheet 7-1 (CPR–Child Older Than 1 Year) on page 142.

Hands-Only CPR

If you are unable or unwilling for any reason to give full CPR (with rescue breaths), you can give hands-only CPR instead. In hands-only CPR, you give continuous chest compressions, with no rescue breaths.

To give hands-only CPR, make sure that 9-1-1 or the local emergency number has been called. Then give chest compressions as you would for full CPR, at a rate of 100 compressions per minute. The only difference is that you do not stop after 30 compressions to give 2 rescue breaths. Continue giving chest compressions until another trained rescuer takes over or until you see an obvious sign of life, such as breathing.

When a child needs CPR, it is better to give full CPR (with rescue breaths) than hands-only CPR. But hands-only CPR may still be of some benefit and is better than doing nothing at all.

Giving CPR to an infant

Giving CPR to a infant is very similar to giving CPR to an older child, with a few key differences:

- Instead of placing your hands in the center of the chest to give compressions, you will use the fingertips of one hand. Place two or three fingers on the center of the infant's chest, just below the nipple line. If you feel the notch at the end of the infant's breastbone, move your fingers slightly toward his head. Place your other hand on the infant's forehead and keep the head tilted back so that the chin is straight up and down (parallel to the floor and ceiling).

- When you give compressions, instead of pushing down about 2 inches as you would in a child, push down only 1½ inches in an infant.

- When you give rescue breaths, instead of pinching the nose shut and covering the mouth with your mouth, cover the infant's nose and mouth with your mouth to form a seal.

For step-by-step instructions on giving CPR to an infant, see Skill Sheet 7-2 (CPR–Infant) on page 144.

AED

Using an AED is the third link in the cardiac chain of survival, after (1) calling 9-1-1 or the local emergency number, and (2) giving CPR. You may have seen an AED at school or in a mall, gym, airport or other public place. An AED is a portable device that can look at the heart's rhythm. If the AED determines that the heart is in an abnormal rhythm that may be "reset" by delivering an electrical shock, it will deliver that shock automatically (or with the push of a button). When used along with CPR, an AED can increase a person's chances of surviving cardiac arrest.

An AED is super easy to use. The machine tells you what to do! To use an AED, just turn the machine on, place the pads on the child's chest, plug the connector cable into the AED (if necessary) and follow the machine's directions. It may tell you to push the "analyze" button to analyze the heart rhythm, or it may just begin to do this by itself. Either way, stand back! No one should touch the child while the AED is analyzing the heart rhythm because this could result in a faulty reading.

Next, the AED may tell you to push the "shock" button, or it may just deliver a shock automatically. Again, stay back! After a shock is delivered (or if the AED decides that no shock is necessary), the AED will continue to check the heart rhythm every 2 minutes. Give 2 minutes of CPR and listen for prompts from the AED. Continue giving CPR and using the AED until you notice an obvious sign of life or until until advanced medical help arrives.

Some AEDs are designed for kids, while other AEDs have special units or pads for kids that are designed to deliver lower levels of energy considered appropriate for children and infants up to 8 years of age or weighing less than 55 pounds. But it's OK to use pads meant for adults on children and infants if special units or pads for kids are not available. The pads are positioned so that one is on the upper right side of the chest and the other is on the left side of the chest. The pads shouldn't touch each other, though, so if the child is too small to position the pads this way without them touching, position one pad in the middle of the child's chest and the other pad on the back between the shoulder blades.

For step-by-step instructions on using an AED, see Skill Sheet 7-3 (Using an AED) on page 146.

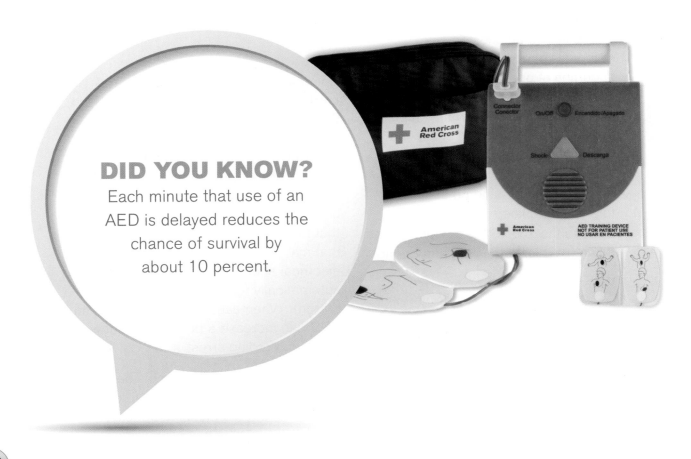

DID YOU KNOW?

Each minute that use of an AED is delayed reduces the chance of survival by about 10 percent.

Breathing Emergencies and Unconscious Choking

So now you know what to do if a child you are caring for experiences a cardiac emergency. But actually, cardiac emergencies are rare in kids younger than 12 years. In kids who are younger than 12 years, it's more likely that the heart will stop beating due to a breathing emergency (like drowning, suffocation or choking). When the body is not getting enough oxygen, the heart soon stops beating, and the child will soon lose consciousness.

For breathing emergencies such as drowning or suffocation, CPR is the lifesaving skill that you will use to provide care until emergency personnel arrive.

However, the care for choking is a little bit different. Remember that when you are checking an unconscious child or infant, you give 2 rescue breaths as part of your check. If the rescue breaths don't go in (that is, they don't cause the chest to rise), then the airway is blocked. In this case, you will begin giving care for an unconscious choking child or infant by using a modified CPR technique (see Skill Sheet 7-1 and Skill Sheet 7-2).

You will learn how to give care to an unconscious choking child or infant in Chapter 8: Basic First Aid for Caregivers.

DID YOU KNOW?

If you are alone with a child who is unconscious and who you did not see collapse, you should give 2 minutes of care (5 CPR cycles) *before* calling for help. This is because under these conditions, the cause of the child's collapse is more likely to be a breathing emergency than a cardiac emergency.

Skill Sheet 7-1: CPR—Child (Older Than 1 Year)

Note: *Use disposable gloves and a breathing barrier to protect yourself from germs.*

1. Place the child on his back on a firm, flat surface. Kneel beside the child.

2. Give **30** chest compressions.

   ■ Place the heel of one hand in the center of the child's chest, with your other hand on top.

   ■ Lean forward so that your shoulders are directly over your hands.

   ■ Keeping your arms straight, push down about 2 inches and then let the chest return to its normal resting position.

   ■ Push hard and push fast! Aim for a rate of 100 compressions per minute.

3. Give **2** rescue breaths.

   ■ Place the breathing barrier over the child's nose and mouth.

   ■ Open the airway. Put one hand on the forehead and two fingers on the bony part of the chin, and tilt the head back until the chin is slightly further back than straight up and down.

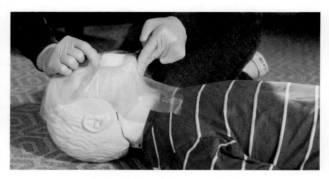

   ■ Pinch the nose shut and make a complete seal over the child's mouth with your mouth.

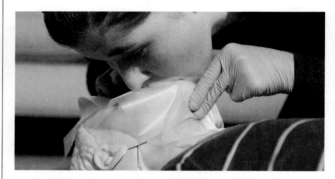

   ■ Take a normal breath and breathe into the child's mouth for about 1 second.

   ■ Release the seal and let the air out, then give the second rescue breath.

Continued on next page

Skill Sheet 7-1: CPR—Child (Older Than 1 Year)

(Continued)

- Each rescue breath should make the chest clearly rise.*

4. Continue giving sets of **30** chest compressions and **2** rescue breaths until:

   - You notice an obvious sign of life, such as breathing.

   - An AED is ready to use.

   - Another trained responder or EMS personnel take over.

   - You are too tired to continue.

   - The scene becomes unsafe.

* If the chest does not clearly rise after the first breath, the airway could be blocked.

1. *Retilt the head and give another rescue breath.*

2. *If the chest still does not rise, give 30 chest compressions.*

3. *Open the mouth to look for and remove a foreign object with your finger, if seen, and then give 2 rescue breaths.*

As long as the chest does not clearly rise, continue cycles of giving 30 chest compressions, looking for a foreign object and giving 2 rescue breaths.

Skill Sheet 7-2: CPR—Infant

Note: *Use disposable gloves and a breathing barrier to protect yourself from germs.*

1. Place the infant on her back on a firm, flat surface.

2. Give **30** chest compressions.

   - Place two or three fingers on the center of the infant's chest, just below the nipple line.

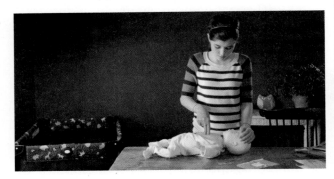

   - Place your other hand on the infant's forehead, and keep the head tilted back so that the chin is straight up and down.

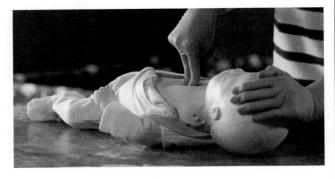

   - Keeping your fingers pointed down, push down about 1½ inches and then let the chest return to its normal resting position.

   - Push hard and push fast! Aim for a rate of 100 compressions per minute.

3. Give **2** rescue breaths.

   - Place the breathing barrier over the infant's nose and mouth.

   - Open the airway. Put one hand on the forehead and two fingers on the bony part of the chin, and tilt the head back until the chin is straight up and down.

   - Make a complete seal over the infant's nose and mouth with your mouth.

   - Take a normal breath, and breathe into the infant's nose and mouth for about 1 second.

   - Release the seal and let the air out, then give the second rescue breath.

     - Each rescue breath should make the chest clearly rise.*

4. Continue giving sets of **30** chest compressions and **2** rescue breaths until:

   - You notice an obvious sign of life, such as breathing.

   - An AED is ready to use.

   - Another trained responder or EMS personnel take over.

   - You are too tired to continue.

   - The scene becomes unsafe.

Continued on next page

Skill Sheet 7-2: CPR—Infant *(Continued)*

* If the chest does not clearly rise after the first breath, the airway could be blocked.

1. *Retilt the head and give another rescue breath.*

2. *If the chest still does not rise, give 30 chest compressions.*

3. *Open the mouth to look for and remove a foreign object with your finger, if seen, and then give 2 rescue breaths.*

As long as the chest does not clearly rise, continue cycles of giving 30 chest compressions, looking for a foreign object and giving 2 rescue breaths.

Skill Sheet 7-3: Using an AED

1. Turn on the AED.

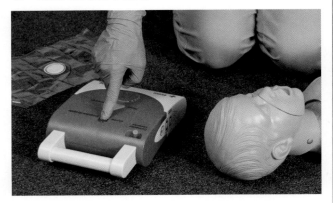

2. Remove the child's shirt and make sure the chest is dry.

3. Place the pads.

   - If you can place both pads on the child's chest without them touching each other, place one pad on the upper right side of the chest and the other on the left side of the chest.

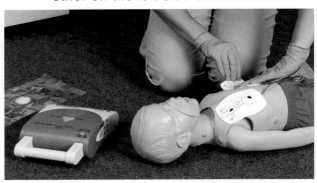

   - If the pads may touch, place one pad in the middle of the child's chest and the other pad on the child's back, between the shoulder blades.

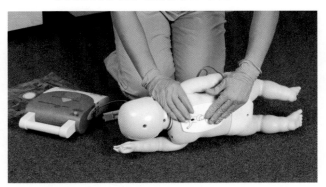

4. Plug the connector cable into the AED, if necessary.

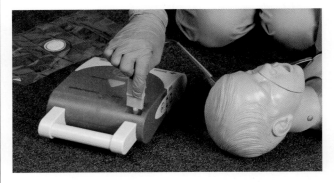

5. Make sure no one, including you, is touching the child. Say, "EVERYONE STAND CLEAR!"

   - Let the AED analyze the heart's rhythm. If the AED tells you to, push the button marked "analyze" to start this process.

   - Let the AED deliver a shock, if it determines one is needed. If the AED tells you to, push the button marked "shock" to deliver the shock.

6. After the AED delivers the shock, or if no shock is advised:

   - Give about 2 minutes of CPR (5 cycles of 30 compressions/2 rescue breaths).

   - Follow the prompts of the AED.

   - Continue giving CPR and following the AED's prompts until you see an obvious sign of life or until help arrives.

FIRST AID FOR CAREGIVERS

So, you've learned the basic steps in any emergency situation: CHECK—CALL—CARE! Now it's time to learn more about the "care" part. Let's take a look at the first aid care you can provide if a child is injured or becomes ill.

Breathing Emergencies

A breathing emergency is *any* respiratory problem that can put a person's life in danger! Breathing emergencies happen when air cannot go freely and easily into the lungs. Asthma and choking are two common breathing emergencies that may occur in children.

Asthma Attacks

Many kids have asthma, an illness that causes trouble breathing. In a person with asthma, "triggers" (such as dust, smoke, air pollution, strong smells, allergies, the weather, exercise, or emotions like stress or fear) can cause the airways in the lungs to suddenly swell. The swelling causes the openings of the airways to become smaller, which makes it harder for air to move in and out of the lungs.

Signals of an asthma attack include wheezing or coughing; rapid, shallow breathing (or trouble breathing); sweating; and being unable to talk without stopping for a breath. The child may tell you that his chest feels tight, or like he can't get enough air into his lungs. Understandably, the child will probably be frightened and upset.

During an asthma attack, reassure the child that you will help. If he is having trouble talking, ask him yes-or-no questions that he can answer by nodding or shaking his head. Have him sit down in the position that is most comfortable and lean forward slightly; this often makes breathing easier. The child may have a "rescue inhaler," which is a device that delivers medication to help open the airways during an asthma attack. If necessary, help him to use the inhaler. Call 9-1-1 or the local emergency number (if you haven't already) if the child's breathing doesn't improve or if the child loses consciousness.

If a child has a rescue inhaler, make sure to talk to the parents about this in advance. There are different types of inhalers. Many kids also use spacers with their inhalers. A spacer is a device that makes it easier for the child to use the inhaler correctly. Ask the parents to show you how the child has been taught to use the inhaler (and spacer, if the child uses one) in case you need to help the child during an asthma attack. It's also a good idea to review the printed instructions on the inhaler so you are familiar with them. For step-by-step instructions on helping a child to use a rescue inhaler, see Skill Sheet 8-1 (Assisting with an Asthma Inhaler) on page 176.

Choking

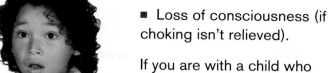

As you know from Chapter 3, choking is common in children younger than 5 years. A child who is choking can quickly stop breathing, become unconscious and die. That's why it's important to act quickly if a child starts to choke. Signals of choking include:

- Clutching the throat with one or both hands.

- A surprised, confused or panicked look on the child's face.

- Coughing, either forcefully or weakly, or being totally unable to cough.

- Being unable to cry or speak.

- High-pitched squeaking noises as the child tries to breathe.

- Bluish skin color.

- Loss of consciousness (if choking isn't relieved).

If you are with a child who starts to choke, first ask the child (if he is old enough) to speak to you or check to see if the child is coughing or crying.

If the child can speak or cry and is coughing forcefully, encourage him to keep coughing. A child who is getting enough air to cough, speak or cry is getting enough air to breathe.

If the child cannot speak or cry and is coughing weakly or making a high-pitched squeaking noise while breathing, the airway is partially blocked and the child is not getting enough air. Have someone call 9-1-1 or the local emergency number immediately and then give first aid for conscious choking. A partially blocked airway can quickly become completely blocked.

If the child is unable to cry, speak, cough or breathe, the airway is completely blocked. The child will lose consciousness quickly unless the airway is cleared. Have someone call 9-1-1 or the local emergency number immediately and then give first aid for conscious choking until the airway is cleared or the child loses consciousness. If the child becomes unconscious, you will need to give first aid for unconscious choking.

First aid for a conscious choking child older than 1 year

When a child older than 1 year is conscious and choking, you give a combination of 5 back blows (strikes between the shoulder blades) followed by 5 abdominal thrusts (upward thrusts just above the belly button). The goal of giving back blows and abdominal thrusts is to force the object out of the child's airway.

- **Back blows.** To give back blows, position yourself to the side and slightly behind the child. Place one arm diagonally across the child's chest (to provide support) and bend her forward at the waist so that her upper body is parallel to the ground. Firmly strike the child between the shoulder blades with the heel of your

other hand. Each back blow should be separate from the others.

- **Abdominal thrusts.** To give abdominal thrusts, stand (or kneel, if the child is small) behind the child and wrap your arms around her waist. Using one or two fingers, find the child's belly button. Make a fist with your other hand and place the thumb side just above the child's belly button. Cover your fist with your other hand and give quick, upward thrusts into the child's abdomen. Each abdominal thrust should be separate from the others.

Continue sets of 5 back blows and 5 abdominal thrusts until the object pops out of the child's mouth; the child can cough forcefully, speak or breathe; or the child becomes unconscious. If the child becomes unconscious, you will need to give first aid for unconscious choking. After the choking incident is over, the child needs to be seen by a doctor, so be sure to tell the parents what happened.

For step-by-step instructions on giving first aid to a conscious child who is older than 1 year and choking, see Skill Sheet

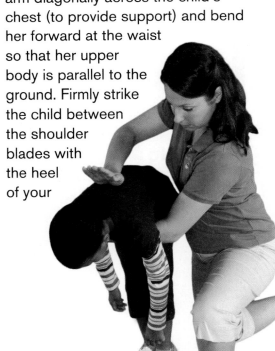

8-2 (Conscious Choking–Child Older Than 1 Year) on page 177.

BE SMART, BE SAFE!

Choking and drowning are breathing emergencies that can be prevented! See Chapter 3 for safety tips to prevent these breathing emergencies.

First aid for a conscious choking infant

When a child younger than 1 year is conscious and choking, you give a combination of 5 back blows followed by 5 chest thrusts (instead of abdominal thrusts). Because an infant can't stand up, you need to turn the infant over as you move from giving back blows to chest thrusts. You can stand, kneel or sit to give first aid to a conscious choking infant. You just need to be able to support the infant on your thigh with her head lower than her chest. If the infant is large, you may find it easiest to sit.

- **Back blows.** First, get the infant into position for back blows. Place your forearm along the infant's back, cradling the back of her head with your hand. Place your other forearm along the infant's front, holding her jaw with your thumb and fingers. Turn the infant over so that she is face-down along your forearm. Lower your arm onto your thigh so that the infant's head is lower than her chest. Continue to hold the infant's jaw with the thumb and fingers of one hand while you firmly strike the infant

between the shoulder blades with the heel of your other hand. Keep your fingers up so that you don't hit the infant's head or neck. Each back blow should be separate from the others.

- **Chest thrusts.** Now, place one hand along the infant's back, cradling the back of her head with your hand.

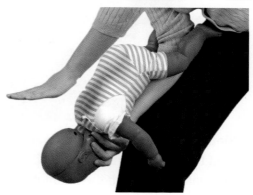

While continuing to hold the infant's jaw with the thumb and fingers of your other hand, support her between your forearms and turn her over so that she is face-up along one forearm. Lower your arm onto your thigh so that the infant's head is lower than her chest. Place the pads of two or three fingers in the center of the infant's chest, on the breastbone. (To find the breastbone, imagine a line across the infant's chest that connects the nipples. Put your fingers just below this imaginary line, in the center of the chest.) Press down 1½ inches and then let the chest return to its normal position. Keep your fingers in contact with the infant's chest.

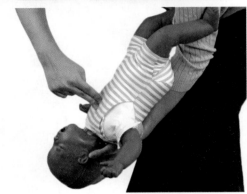

Continue sets of 5 back blows and 5 chest thrusts until the object pops out of the infant's mouth; the infant can cough forcefully, cry or breathe; or the infant becomes unconscious. If the infant becomes unconscious, you will need to give first aid for unconscious choking. After the choking incident is over, the infant needs to be seen by a doctor, so be sure to tell the parents what happened.

For step-by-step instructions on giving first aid to a conscious infant who is choking, see Skill Sheet 8-3 (Conscious Choking–Infant) on page 178.

First aid for unconscious choking

In some choking situations, you may see the child or infant lose consciousness. If this happens, lower the child to the floor or place the infant on a hard, flat surface and begin using the modified CPR technique.

The modified CPR technique is the same as regular CPR, except that you look for (and remove, if seen) the object that is blocking the airway between compressions and breaths. To look for the object:

- Grasp the child's lower jaw between your thumb and forefinger and open the mouth.

- Look for the object.

- If you see the object, remove it with your pinky finger. If the child is bigger than normal you may need to use your index finger.

Don't put your finger inside the child's mouth unless you can actually see the object! If you can't see the object and you just put your finger in the child's mouth, you might accidentally push the object deeper into the child's airway.

For step-by-step instructions on giving first aid to an unconscious choking child who is older than 1 year, see Skill Sheet 8-4 (Unconscious Choking–Child Older Than 1 Year) on page 179. For step-by-step instructions on giving first aid to an unconscious choking infant, see Skill Sheet 8-5 (Unconscious Choking–Infant) on page 180.

Sudden Illness

Everyone gets sick, and sometimes illnesses come on suddenly. There are lots of reasons a child could suddenly start to feel sick, ranging from coming down with the flu, to spending too much time outside on a hot day, to a flare-up of a chronic condition, like diabetes or asthma.

When a child becomes suddenly ill, he usually looks or acts sick, or acts differently than normal. A child who is ill may have:

- An upset stomach, such as feeling like throwing up (nausea), actually throwing up (vomiting), or having diarrhea.

- A stomachache. (An infant with a stomachache may cry uncontrollably, curl up or just generally look uncomfortable.)

- A headache.

- Pale or very flushed skin, which may be sweaty or very dry.

- A fever.

- Dizziness or light-headedness, possibly leading to fainting.

- Trouble breathing.

- Problems seeing or speaking (for example, blurry vision or slurred speech).

- Numbness, weakness or paralysis (an inability to move).

- Seizures.

- Loss of consciousness.

Luckily, you don't have to know exactly what is wrong in order to help the child feel better until his parents get home (or, if his symptoms are serious, emergency responders arrive). If a child becomes ill, first check the scene for clues about what might be wrong, and then check the child. Provide care according to the signals that you find and your level of training. Signals like trouble breathing; problems seeing or speaking; numbness, weakness or paralysis; seizures; or loss of consciousness require a call to 9-1-1 or the local emergency number. Calm and reassure the child, help him rest in a comfortable position, and keep him from getting too chilled or overheated. Closely watch the child's breathing and consciousness until the parents return home or emergency responders arrive. In addition to the illnesses discussed below, see Appendix D for information on other sudden illnesses (Cardiac Emergency, Stroke).

Stomach Troubles

Stomach troubles (such as a stomachache, feeling queasy, throwing up or having diarrhea) occur frequently in children. Common causes of stomach troubles in kids include infections and food-related problems (like food poisoning, eating too much or eating a food that "doesn't agree" with them). When a child is having stomach troubles, it is best to avoid giving him anything to eat. The child probably won't feel much like eating anyway!

- **Stomachaches.** Common causes of stomachaches include constipation and excess gas, as well as food-related problems and infections. Usually, stomachaches aren't serious and they will go away on their own. If the child tells you that her tummy hurts, reassure her and try to keep her comfortable. Call the parents and follow any instructions they may give you.

- **Vomiting.** If a child throws up (or tells you she feels like she is going to throw up), do what you can to keep the child comfortable. If the child has already been sick, clean the inside of her mouth, and wipe her lips and

face with damp towel. (Remember to put on your disposable gloves first!) Change her clothes or sheets, if necessary. Help her to lie down in a comfortable position on her side so she does not inhale or swallow vomit. Keep a large bowl or a bucket nearby in case she needs to throw up again. If the child does get sick again, help her to sit up and support her while she is sick. Tell her everything will be OK. Call the parents, and ask them if there is anything else you should do until they get home. Vomiting can lead to dehydration, especially in young children and babies, so keep track of the number of times the child vomits and be sure to tell the parents when they get home. Halt solids foods for 24 hours and slowly replace with clear fluids and liquids. Gradually reintroduce the child's normal diet.

BE SMART, BE SAFE! An infant younger than 3 months who is vomiting or has diarrhea needs to see the health care provider right away. A child older than 3 months needs to see a health care provider if he is vomiting for more than 12 hours, cannot retain liquids or replace lost liquids, or has diarrhea that persists for more than 2 days or leads to dehydration.

- **Diarrhea.** The care for diarrhea is much the same as it is for vomiting. Make sure the child is clean and comfortable, and call the parents for additional instructions. Be sure to note how many times the child had diarrhea during the time that you were there because diarrhea can also lead to dehydration.

Fever

Fever is a common signal of illness in children. When a child has a fever, his skin will feel warm or hot. Fever is often accompanied by other signals of illness, such as a headache, muscle aches, chills, loss of appetite, low energy, difficulty sleeping and vomiting. An infant who has a fever may seem fussy, or he may be quiet and not as active as usual.

DID YOU KNOW?

Raising the body temperature a couple of degrees helps activate the body's immune system to make more white blood cells, antibodies, and other infection-fighting agents as well as making it harder for the bacteria or viruses to survive.

The best way to find out if a child has a fever is to take his temperature. When you meet with the parents before taking a caregiving job, ask them what thermometer they would like you to use if you need to take the child's temperature, and ask them to show you how to use it. There are many different types of thermometers meant for taking temperatures in different parts of the body.

- **Digital thermometers** are placed under the tongue or in the armpit.

- **Tympanic thermometers** are inserted into the ear.

- **Temporal thermometers** are passed across the forehead.

Always use the thermometer and method of taking the temperature that the parents tell you to use. The right method to use depends on the child's age. As a general guideline:

If the Child Is:	Use a:
Younger than 6 months	Digital thermometer placed in the armpit
Between the ages of 6 months and 4 years	Tympanic thermometer placed in the ear **OR** Temporal thermometer passed across the forehead
4 years or older	Tympanic thermometer placed in the ear **OR** Temporal thermometer passed across the forehead **OR** Digital thermometer placed under the tongue

For step-by-step instructions on using various types of thermometers, see Skill Sheet 8-6 (Taking a Temperature) on page 182. Also, read the directions that are with the thermometer you are using to make sure that you are using it correctly.

A fever is defined as an elevated body temperature above the normal range of 97.7–99.5° F (36.5–37.5° C). If a child develops a fever, call the parents right away so they are aware of the fever and can give you instructions on what to do. If you think the child might have a fever but you don't feel comfortable taking the child's temperature (or the parents have asked you not to), you should also call the parents. Infants younger than 3 months with any fever, infants between 3 and 6 months with a temperature of 101° F or higher, and children older than 6 months with a temperature of 102° F or higher need to be seen by a health care provider. In these cases, the parents should come home right away.

Febrile Seizures

In babies and young children, a high fever can cause a seizure (called a febrile seizure). The child may lose consciousness and shake uncontrollably during the seizure. Although febrile seizures can be frightening to watch, the vast majority only last for 1 to 2 minutes and do not cause any harm. If a child has a febrile seizure, provide care as you would for any other type of seizure and make sure the parents have been called. Call 9-1-1 or the local emergency number if this is the first time the child has had a febrile seizure, the seizure lasts longer than 5 minutes or is repeated, or the seizure is followed by a quick rise in the temperature of the child or infant.

Allergic Reactions

Our immune systems help to keep us healthy by fighting off harmful things, like germs. But sometimes, our immune systems overreact and try to fight off ordinary things that aren't usually harmful, like certain foods, grass, or pet dander (tiny flakes of skin that animals shed). A person can have an allergy to almost anything. Common allergies include allergies to bee stings, certain foods (like nuts or shellfish), animal dander, plant pollen, certain medications (like penicillin and antibiotic ointments) and latex (found in some protective gloves).

An allergic reaction can range from mild to very severe. A person who is having a mild to moderate allergic reaction may develop a skin rash, a stuffy nose or red, watery eyes. A person who is having a severe, life-threatening allergic reaction (called *anaphylaxis*) may develop one or more of the following signals within seconds or minutes of coming into contact with the substance:

- Trouble breathing

- Swelling of the face, neck or tongue

- A feeling of tightness in the chest or throat

- A rash or hives (large red itchy bumps) that cover the entire body

- An upset stomach (pain, vomiting or diarrhea)

- Dizziness

- Shock

- Loss of consciousness

If a child is known to have an allergy that could lead to anaphylaxis, he may have

an auto-injector. An auto-injector is a pen-like device that contains a needle and a dose of epinephrine that will slow or stop the effects of a severe allergic reaction. Pushing the auto-injector against the outer thigh injects the medication into the muscle and the body.

If you care for a child who has a severe allergy, ask the parents if the child has an auto-injector and if they want you to help the child use it if he has a severe allergic reaction and is unable to use the auto-injector to give the medication himself. If the parents say it is OK for you to help the child with the auto-injector, ask them to show you how to use it. Also, make sure you know where the auto-injector is kept and that you take it with you if you and the child leave the house for any reason.

If a child you are caring for has an allergic reaction, watch the child carefully for signals of breathing problems. If you know that the child has had a severe allergic reaction before, or if the child is having trouble breathing or showing any other signals of a severe allergic reaction, call 9-1-1 or the local emergency number immediately. If the child has an auto-injector, encourage him to use it on himself. If he can't, you may need to help, because it is important to act fast when a child is having a severe allergic reaction that affects his ability to breathe. For step-by-step instructions on helping a child to use an auto-injector, see Skill Sheet 8-7 (Assisting with an Epinephrine Auto-Injector) on page 184.

Blood Sugar (Diabetic) Emergencies

Diabetes is a condition that makes it difficult for the body to process sugar in the blood. A child with diabetes can become ill when there is too little or too much sugar in his blood. A child with diabetes who is having a blood sugar emergency will seem generally ill. He may feel dizzy or shaky, have a headache, or have cool, clammy skin. His behavior may change (for example, he may become cranky). If the levels of sugar in his blood are extremely high or extremely low, the child may have seizures and become unconscious. This is a life-threatening situation and you should call 9-1-1 or the local emergency number immediately.

If you will be caring for a child who has diabetes, the child's parents should tell you what to do if the child has a blood sugar emergency. Many kids with diabetes will recognize that they are

having a low blood sugar emergency, and they may ask you for something with sugar in it. If the child is a known diabetic, is alert and can safely swallow, give him a form of sugar, such as:

- Glucose tablets or gel tube (follow package instructions).

- 2 tablespoons) of raisins.

- 4 ounces (½ cup) of juice or regular soda (nondiet).

- 1 tablespoon sugar, honey or corn syrup.

- 8 ounces of nonfat or 1 percent milk.

- Hard candies, jellybeans or gumdrops.

Have the child check his blood sugar level, if he knows how. If the child is not feeling better in about 5 minutes, call 9-1-1 or the local emergency number.

Seizures

The brain communicates with the other parts of the body by sending out electrical signals. A seizure occurs when there is unusual electrical activity in the brain. A person who is having a seizure may lose consciousness or shake uncontrollably.

Seizures can have different causes. One common cause in small children is a fever. Another common cause is a condition called epilepsy. Children with epilepsy usually take medication to reduce the number of seizures they have, but seizures may still occur. If you care for a child with epilepsy, ask the parents what you should do if he has a seizure.

Although a seizure can be frightening to see, it's easy to care for a child who is having a seizure. Don't try to hold on to the child, or to stop the seizure from happening. Just let the seizure run its course. Most seizures only last a few minutes. First, call 9-1-1 or the local emergency number. If the child has a condition that is known to cause seizures, such as epilepsy, the parents may prefer that you call them instead of the emergency number. Then, take steps to protect the child from injury during the seizure. Move furniture or other objects that could cause injury out of the way.

BE SMART, BE SAFE! You may have heard that you should put something between the teeth of a person who is having a seizure to prevent the person from biting her own tongue, but this is unsafe. Never try to put anything in the mouth of a person who is having a seizure.

When the seizure is over, check the child like you would an unconscious child. Make sure her airway is open. Usually, the child will be breathing normally. If there is fluid in the child's mouth (such as pooled saliva, blood or vomit), roll the child onto her side so that the fluid drains from her mouth. Comfort and stay with the child until she is fully conscious or the emergency responders arrive.

Fainting

If a child suddenly loses consciousness and then "comes to" after about a minute or two, she may simply have fainted. Fainting is caused by a sudden decrease in blood flow to the brain. Usually, the cause of fainting is not serious. For example, being dehydrated (not having enough fluid in the body), being too hot or being in a crowded room can cause a person to faint. After the person faints and is lying down, the head is at the same level as the heart. This helps blood flow return to the brain and the person quickly recovers.

A child who is about to faint often becomes pale, begins to sweat and may feel weak or dizzy. The child may faint before you even know what is happening, but sometimes it is possible to prevent a fainting spell by having the child sit down with her head between her knees. If the child does faint, lower her to the ground

and position her on her back. Loosen any tight clothing and check to make sure she is breathing. If the child vomits, roll her onto her side. Once the child recovers, check her from toe to head for any injuries that might have happened as a result of the fall, and give care according to the conditions that you find and your level of training. Call the parents and let them know what happened. Although the cause of fainting is not usually serious, the parents may still want to follow up with the child's doctor.

Poisoning

A child who has been poisoned may have symptoms that are similar to those caused by other types of illnesses, such as stomach upset or pain, headache, dizziness, drowsiness, loss of consciousness, trouble breathing, sweating or seizures. Your best clue as to what is wrong will come from checking the scene and the child. Is there an open or spilled container (medicine, cleaning products) or an overturned or damaged plant nearby? Are there any unusual odors? Do you see traces of what the child put in her mouth on her face, or smell a strange odor on her breath? Are others in the house sick? Are pets sick?

If you suspect that a child has been poisoned, call the National Poison Control

Center (PCC) Hotline at 800-222-1222 and follow the dispatcher's instructions. (But if the child is unconscious, having trouble breathing or having a seizure, call 9-1-1 or the local emergency number first!) If possible, tell the dispatcher what the poison was, how much the child swallowed and when the child swallowed it. Don't give the child anything to eat or drink unless the dispatcher tells you to. If the child vomits, position her in a recovery position.

Environmental Emergencies

Children love to play outside! There are so many fun things to do—hiking, playing sports, playing on a playground or just running around a park. However, playing outside may also mean exposure to extreme temperatures or stinging and biting insects and animals. Despite your best prevention efforts, a child may become overheated or too cold; or she may get stung by a bee or bitten by a neighbor's dog. Let's see what you should do if one of these emergencies happens. In addition to the environmental injuries discussed below, see Appendix D for information on other environmental emergencies (Scorpion Sting; Snake Bites, Venomous).

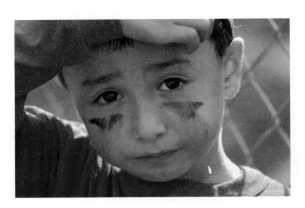

Heat-Related Illnesses

Our bodies work to keep our internal body temperature pretty constant, at around 98.6° F. For example, sweating is one way the body cools itself, and shivering is one way the body warms itself up. But sometimes the body's heating and cooling systems aren't able to keep up, and this can make a person sick. It may even cause death.

Heat-related illnesses, such as heat cramps, heat exhaustion or heat stroke, occur when the body is unable to keep itself cool. A child who is playing outside on a warm day can easily develop a heat-

related illness, especially if the child isn't drinking a lot of fluids. If you think a child is developing a heat-related illness, first move her to a cooler place. Then give first aid according to the conditions that you find.

- **Heat cramps** are painful muscle spasms, usually in the legs and stomach. Heat cramps can turn into heat exhaustion or heat stroke, so you need to act accordingly. Move the child to a cooler place, and give him small sips of a noncarbonated sports drink, milk, juice or water. Lightly stretch the muscle and gently rub the area to relieve the cramps. Often this is enough for the body to recover, but watch for signals of heat exhaustion or heat stroke.

- **Heat exhaustion** occurs when the body's cooling system is not able to keep up. The child's skin may be cool and moist, and either very pale or gray, or red. The child may be sweating heavily and may complain of having a headache, feeling sick to his stomach or being dizzy. If a child has been out in the heat and shows any of these signals, move him to a shaded or cooler place. Loosen or remove as much clothing as possible, and apply cool, wet towels or clothes to the skin or spray the child with cool water. Fanning the child may also help as this increases evaporative cooling. Applying ice packs or commercial cold packs wrapped in a thin towel to the wrist, ankles, armpits, groin and back of the neck may cool the blood in the major blood vessels, if further cooling down is required. If the child is conscious, you can give him small sips of a sports drink, milk, juice or water. If the child does not improve quickly, refuses to drink, vomits, loses consciousness or shows signals of heat stroke, send someone to call 9-1-1 or the local emergency number and give care for heat stroke.

- **Heat stroke** is the most severe form of heat-related illness. It occurs when the body's cooling system is completely overwhelmed and stops working properly. Heat stroke is life threatening! The child's skin may be hot and wet or dry. The child may seem confused or lose consciousness. His breathing may be rapid and shallow, and his pulse may be rapid and weak. The child may vomit. If you suspect heat stroke, call 9-1-1 or the local emergency number. Remove or loosen tight

clothing and begin to rapidly cool the body. Cold-water immersion is the fastest and recommended cooling method. However, until medical help arrives, you can douse or spray the person with cold water or sponge the person with ice water-doused towels over the entire body, frequently rotating the cold, wet towels. If the child becomes unconscious, be prepared to give CPR.

Cold-Related Illnesses

Cold-related illnesses include hypothermia and frostbite.

Hypothermia

Hypothermia occurs when the entire body cools because its ability to keep warm fails. Hypothermia can lead to death if it is not treated.

Signals of hypothermia include shivering, a "glassy" stare, numbness, weakness, indifference and impaired judgment. The child may lose consciousness. To give first aid for hypothermia, move the child to a warmer place. Remove any wet clothing and dry the child. Help the child to warm up gradually by helping her to put on dry clothing (including a hat, gloves and socks) and wrapping her in a blanket. If the child is alert and able to swallow, you can give her small sips of a warm liquid. If the child is unconscious or does not seem to be responding to first aid, call 9-1-1 or the local emergency number. Shivering that stops without rewarming is a sign that the person's condition is worsening. He or she needs immediate medical care.

BE SMART, BE SAFE!

Although you might think a hot bath or shower would help to warm the child up, this is a bad idea. Putting the child in a hot bath or shower can cause the body to rewarm too quickly, leading to dangerous heart rhythms.

Frostbite

Frostbite is freezing of body parts that are exposed to cold temperatures. Frostbite can cause the loss of fingers, hands, arms, toes, feet and legs. The frostbitten area is numb, and the skin is cold to the touch and appears waxy. The skin may be white, yellow, blue or red. In severe cases, there may be blisters and the skin may turn black.

To give first aid for frostbite, first get the child out of the cold. Don't try to rewarm the area if there is a chance that the frostbitten area could freeze again. Also, don't try to rewarm the area if the frostbite is severe (the skin is blistered or black). Call 9-1-1 or the local emergency number and take actions to prevent hypothermia.

If the frostbite is minor (no blisters), gradually rewarm the frostbitten part by cupping it in your warm hands to create skin-to-skin contact. Handle the frostbitten area gently. Don't rub it—rubbing can cause more injury! When the frostbitten part has thawed out, loosely bandage the area with dry sterile gauze. If fingers or toes were frostbitten, place dry sterile gauze between them to keep them separated. Let the parents know what happened so that they can follow up with the child's doctor.

DID YOU KNOW?

Although a common cause of hypothermia is cold weather, the air temperature does not have to be below freezing for hypothermia to occur. This is especially true if the child is wet, or if there is wind. For example, a child who is wet from swimming could develop hypothermia, even in the summertime!

Bites and Stings

Bites and stings are common, especially when kids are playing outside during the warmer months.

Bee stings

Yee-oww! It hurts to get stung by a bee or one of its relatives, like a yellow jacket or wasp! If a bee stings a child, here's how you can help the child to feel better. First, use a plastic card (like your driver's license or a credit card) to scrape the stinger away from the skin. Wash the area with soap and warm water, and pat dry. If the parents told you it was OK to use antibiotic ointment, you can apply a little bit before covering the site with an adhesive bandage. To reduce swelling and pain, apply a commercial cold pack or an ice pack wrapped in a thin towel to the site.

For many kids, a bee sting is just painful and frightening. But for kids who are allergic, a bee sting can cause a serious, potentially life-threatening allergic reaction called *anaphylaxis.* Parents who know that their child is allergic to bee stings will probably tell you this when you meet with them before taking the caregiving job. They may also give you specific instructions about how you can help the child if he is stung by a bee. But sometimes, parents may not know that their child is allergic to bee stings. This may be the first time the child has been stung, or the child may not have had an allergic reaction in the past. So watch the child closely for signals of a serious allergic reaction, such as trouble breathing. If the child shows signals of a serious allergic reaction, call 9-1-1 or the local emergency number right away.

Tick bites

Although tick bites are not painful at all, they can make people very sick. Ticks are little blood-suckers that attach themselves to the skin. While they are sucking their victim's blood, they can spread germs from their mouths into the victim's body. These germs can cause serious diseases, such as Lyme disease and Rocky Mountain spotted fever.

After coming in from playing outdoors, you should always check the kids for ticks. Most experts believe that the longer a tick stays attached to the skin, the greater the chances are of infection, so if you find a tick, remove it. Put on your disposable gloves. Using fine-tipped, pointed, nonetched, nonrasped (smooth inside surface) tweezers, grasp the tick at the head, as close to the skin as possible. Pull slowly, steadily and firmly without twisting. Seal the tick in a container with rubbing alcohol to kill it, and then save the container. (This helps with identifying the type of tick later.) Wash the area with soap and warm water and then apply a little bit of antibiotic ointment if the parents told you it was OK to use.

Be sure to tell the parents about the tick because they will need to watch the child for several days to make sure he doesn't develop an infection. You should also tell the parents if you weren't able to remove the tick, or if you think that the tick's mouth parts are still in the child's skin. In this case, the parents will definitely need to take the child to the doctor.

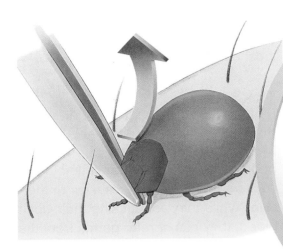

Spider bites

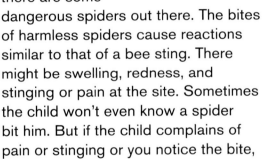

Most spiders are harmless, although there are some dangerous spiders out there. The bites of harmless spiders cause reactions similar to that of a bee sting. There might be swelling, redness, and stinging or pain at the site. Sometimes the child won't even know a spider bit him. But if the child complains of pain or stinging or you notice the bite, give first aid as you would for a bee sting: wash the area, apply antibiotic ointment (if the parents told you it was OK to use) and an adhesive bandage, and then apply a commercial cold pack or an ice pack wrapped in a dry towel to reduce pain and swelling.

Dangerous Creepy Crawlies

Few spiders in the United States can cause serious illness or death. However, the bites of the black widow and brown recluse spiders can, in rare cases, kill a child. Another dangerous spider is the northwestern brown (hobo) spider. These spiders prefer dark, out-of-the-way places, such as wood, rock and brush piles; dark garages; and attics. Children may be bitten on their arms and hands when reaching into these places.

Scorpions are related to spiders. They live under rocks, logs and the bark of certain trees and are most active at night. Like spiders, only a few species of scorpions have a sting that can cause death, but it is hard to tell a poisonous scorpion from one that is harmless.

Continued on next page

Dangerous Creepy Crawlies *(Continued)*

If you think that a child may have been bitten by a poisonous spider or stung by a scorpion, immediately call 9-1-1 or the local emergency number!

Dangerous Creepy Crawly	Usually Found In	Poisonous Effects
Brown recluse 	Midwestern and southeastern United States 	At first, the bite may not cause any pain, or it may only sting (like a bee sting). Over 1 to 8 hours, the site becomes very painful and itchy. A blood-filled blister forms under the surface of the skin, sometimes in a bull's eye pattern. Over time, the blister increases in size and eventually ruptures, causing an open sore. The child may have signals similar to those caused by the flu (nausea, vomiting, fever, muscle pain).
Black widow 	Throughout the United States, but most common in the southern states 	At first, the bite causes a sharp pain like a pinprick, followed by a dull pain. Within 20 minutes to 1 hour, the child will start to feel ill. Signals include muscle cramps and weakness; stomach pain, nausea and vomiting; dizziness or fainting; chest pain; and trouble breathing.
Northwestern brown (hobo) 	Northwestern United States 	A hobo spider bite causes an open, slow-healing wound.
Scorpion 	Throughout the United States, especially in the warmer southwestern states 	A scorpion sting causes pain, tingling, burning and numbness at the site. Life-threatening symptoms that affect the whole body (such as numbness, trouble breathing and seizures) may develop.

Animal bites

A family pet, a neighbor's pet, or a stray or wild animal may bite a child. Dog bites may rip the skin and cause a lot of bleeding. Cat bites are more likely to cause puncture wounds. Puncture wounds, which occur when a sharp, pointed object (like a cat's tooth) pierces the skin, usually don't bleed much but they are difficult to clean and often become infected.

If an animal bites a child you are caring for, try to get the child away from the animal without putting yourself in danger. Do not try to hold or catch the animal. If the wound appears to be minor and was caused by an animal that the child

knows (such as the family pet), clean it and care for it as you would any other wound, but be sure to let the parents know what happened so they can watch for infection. If the wound is severe or caused by a wild or stray animal, call 9-1-1 or the local emergency number and take steps to control the bleeding.

Rabies

Rabies is a serious infection that attacks the brain and spinal cord and causes death if it is not treated. The virus that causes rabies is spread when an animal that has the disease bites another animal or a person. Wild animals (such as foxes, skunks, bats and raccoons) can carry rabies. Pets (like cats and dogs) and livestock (like cattle) can also carry rabies, if they are not vaccinated against it.

Animals with rabies may act strangely. For example, those that are usually active at night may be active in the daytime. A wild animal that usually tries to avoid people might not run from you. Rabid animals may drool, appear to be partially paralyzed, or act aggressively or strangely quiet.

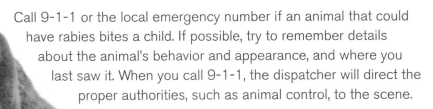

Call 9-1-1 or the local emergency number if an animal that could have rabies bites a child. If possible, try to remember details about the animal's behavior and appearance, and where you last saw it. When you call 9-1-1, the dispatcher will direct the proper authorities, such as animal control, to the scene.

A person who is bitten by an animal that might have rabies must get medical attention immediately. Treatment for rabies includes a series of injections to build up immunity that will help fight the disease.

Soft Tissue Injuries

Injuries—such as cuts and scrapes, bumps and bruises, and burns—may happen, despite your best efforts to prevent them. Active kids are bound to hurt themselves once in a while! Many times, these injuries aren't serious and you'll be able to "make it all better" with some first aid and a hug. Other times, the injuries will be more serious and may require a trip to the emergency room or doctor's office. Let's take a look at what you should do when some common injuries occur. In addition to the injuries discussed below, see Appendix D for information on other soft tissue injuries (Blister, Object Stuck in Body, Splinter, Tooth Knocked Out).

Bleeding

Bruises, scraped knees and bloody noses are part of growing up. More serious injuries that cause lots of bleeding can also occur.

Bruises

Bruises are caused by bleeding under the surface of the skin. The area may appear red or purple, and there may be swelling. The bruised area is often painful. Applying a commercial cold pack can help to reduce the pain and swelling. If you don't have a commercial cold pack, you can put ice in a plastic bag or even use a bag of frozen peas from the freezer. Before applying a commercial cold pack or an ice pack to the child's skin, wrap it

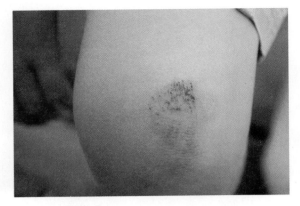

in a dry towel. This helps to protect the skin from injury due to the cold. Hold the commercial cold pack or ice pack in place for no more than 20 minutes. Wait at least an hour before applying ice again. Raising the bruised area (for example, by putting pillows under the arm or leg with the bruise) may also help to reduce swelling. (But don't raise the bruised area if raising the area causes the child pain.)

Cuts and scrapes

Minor cuts and scrapes often stop bleeding on their own in a few minutes, but you need to clean the area carefully so that the cut or scrape doesn't get infected. Put on your disposable gloves and apply direct pressure with a gauze pad to stop the bleeding. When the bleeding stops, wash the area with soap and warm water. Rinse under warm running water for about 5 minutes, and then dry the area. If the parents told you it was OK to use antibiotic ointment, you can apply a little bit to the cut or scrape. Then cover the cut or scrape with an adhesive bandage. Remember to wash your own hands after you've finished taking care of the cut or scrape, even if you wore disposable gloves.

More serious injuries, such as a deep cut, may bleed a lot more. If the wound is bleeding heavily, cover the area with a gauze pad and apply direct pressure with your gloved hand until the bleeding stops. This may take as long as 15 minutes. Do not lift the pad because lifting the pad may cause the bleeding to start again. If blood soaks through the gauze pad, just put another gauze pad on top of the first and keep applying pressure. When the bleeding slows or stops, make a bandage by wrapping roll gauze around the wound several times to hold the gauze pads in place. Tie or tape the bandage to secure it. The bandage should be snug, but not too tight. Check the skin on the side of the injury farthest away from the heart—the skin should be warm and its normal color. If the skin is cool or pale, the area is swollen, or the child tells you that the area is numb or has a "tingly" feeling, then the bandage is too tight!

If after 15 minutes the bleeding has not stopped, call 9-1-1 or the local emergency number if you haven't already done so. If blood soaks through the bandage, apply additional gauze pads and bandages on top of the first as needed, and continue to apply pressure. Be alert to signals that the child's condition is worsening, such as faster or slower breathing, changes in skin color (pale, ashen, bluish) and restlessness and anxiety. These could be signals of shock, a life-threatening condition (see Chapter 6). Have the child rest comfortably and keep him from becoming too hot or too cold. Reassure him that help is on the way.

For step-by-step instructions on controlling severe bleeding, see Skill Sheet 8-8 (Controlling Severe Bleeding) on page 185.

Nosebleeds

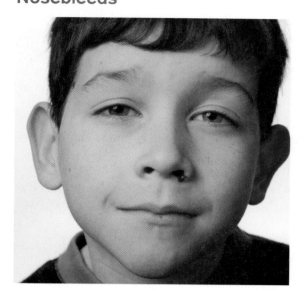

Kids may get a nosebleed after falling or getting hit on the nose. Sometimes, just breathing dry air (for example, in the wintertime) is enough to start a nosebleed. If a child develops a nosebleed, here's what to do. Have the child sit down and lean slightly forward. If the child is old enough, you can ask him to pinch his nostrils together, or you can do this for the child (remember to put on your disposable gloves first!). Keep the nostrils pinched shut for at least 5 minutes before checking to see if the bleeding has stopped. If it hasn't stopped after 5 minutes, keep pinching the nostrils shut for another 5 minutes. If after 20 minutes the bleeding has not stopped, hold a commercial cold pack or an ice pack wrapped in a towel against the bridge of the nose, while continue to pinch the nostrils shut. Having the child suck on a piece of ice may be useful in slowing down blood flow; be sure to continue to pinch the nostrils shut. Most nosebleeds stop after 10 to 15 minutes. If the nosebleed continues for more than 15 to 20 minutes, or if the bleeding is severe or gushing, call 9-1-1 or the local emergency number. Remember to wash your hands after you've finished taking care of the nosebleed, even if you wore disposable gloves!

Burns

There are many different causes of burns. Usually, when we think about burns we think about those caused by the sun or by contact with hot liquids, surfaces or flames (such as scald burns). But did you know that chemicals and electricity can also cause burns?

Burns can be minor or life threatening. How serious a burn is depends on how deep it is and how much of the body is burned. Burned skin can appear red, brown, black or white. The burned area may be extremely painful or almost painless (if the burn is deep enough to destroy the nerve endings that let us feel pain). There may be swelling, blisters or both. The blisters may break and ooze a clear fluid.

First aid for a burn involves three major steps:

STOP COVER COOL

- **Stop!** First, stop the burning. If the burn is caused by heat, remove the source of the heat. For example, if a child's clothes are on fire, have the child "stop, drop and roll" to put out the flames. If the burn is caused by chemicals, put on gloves and brush the chemical off the skin (if the chemical is a powder) or rinse the area with cool running water for at least 20 minutes (if the chemical is a liquid). Also, take off any of the child's clothing that may be contaminated with the chemical. If the burn is caused by electricity, turn off the power at its source (such as the main circuit breaker).

- **Cool!** Next, cool the burn by rinsing it with large amounts of cool running water. This will help to relieve pain. Never use ice to cool a burn; this can cause more damage to the skin.

- **Cover!** Cover the burn loosely with sterile gauze.

It's important to know when to call 9-1-1 or the local emergency number for a burn. In general, you should call the emergency number if the burn:

- Involves a child, unless the burn is very minor.

- Involves the head, neck, mouth or nose or causes difficulty breathing.

- Involves the hands, feet or groin.

- Covers more than one part of the body or covers a large percentage of the body.

- Involves a complete circle around the body or a limb.

- Was caused by chemicals, electricity or an explosion.

Burns of all types, especially if they cover a large percentage of the body, can cause a person to go into shock. If the burn was caused by electricity, you also need to be prepared to give CPR, because the electrical current can affect the heart and breathing.

BE SMART, BE SAFE!

Remember what you learned in Chapter 6 about checking the scene for safety! Never enter a scene if doing so will put you in danger too.

Muscle, Bone and Joint Injuries

Muscle, bone and joint injuries are very common in children. Children are extremely active and love to run, jump, climb trees and take risks! Despite your best efforts at prevention and constant watch over the child for whom you are caring, accidents can still happen!

Injuries to the muscles, bones and joints include sprains (such as a twisted ankle); strains (an overstretched muscle); dislocations; fractures (broken bones); head, neck and spinal injuries; and concussions. These injuries range from minor and uncomfortable, to serious and very painful, to life-threatening injuries in which the child loses consciousness. Learning how to care for these types of injuries is essential!

Sprains, Strains, Dislocations and Fractures

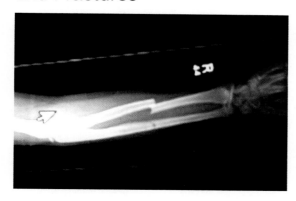

Sprains, strains, dislocations and fractures can be extremely painful injuries.

- A *sprain* occurs when a ligament is stretched or torn. Ligaments connect bones to bones at the joints.

- A *strain* occurs when a tendon or muscle is stretched or torn. Tendons connect muscles to bones.

- A *dislocation* occurs when the bones that meet at a joint move out of their normal position.

- A *fracture* is a complete break, a chip or a crack in a bone.

Sometimes, the injury will be very obvious—for example, you may see the ends of a broken bone poking through the skin, or the injured body part might appear bent or crooked. Other times, the only signals of injury may be swelling or bruising. Usually, the child will try to avoid using the injured body part because using it causes pain. The child might also tell you he felt or heard a "popping," "snapping" or "grating" noise at the time of the injury.

You don't need to worry about trying to figure out exactly what kind of muscle, bone or joint injury has occurred. The general first aid steps are the same for all types of muscle, bone and joint injuries. Just remember "RICE":

- **R** stands for **rest.** Don't allow the child to use the injured body part and avoid any movements or activities that cause pain.

- **I** stands for **immobilize.** Keep the injured body part in the position it was found.

- **C** stands for **cold.** Apply a commercial cold pack or an ice pack wrapped in a dry, thin towel to the area to reduce swelling and pain. Apply the commercial cold pack or ice pack for no more than 20 minutes at a time, and wait at least

Muscle, Bone or Joint Injuries: When Do I Call 9-1-1?

Sometimes when a child has a muscle, bone or joint injury, you'll be able to tell right away that you need to call 9-1-1 or the local emergency number. But not all muscle, bone or joint injuries result in obvious injuries, and some aren't serious enough to require a call to the emergency number. Here's when to call:

- A broken bone is poking through the skin.

- The injured body part is bent, crooked or looks deformed.

- There is moderate or severe swelling and bruising.

- The child heard or felt a "popping," "snapping" or "grating" sound at the time of the injury.

- The child cannot move or use the injured body part.

- The injured area is cold and numb.

- The injury involves the head, neck or spine.

- The child is having trouble breathing.

- The cause of the injury (for example, a fall from a tree or getting hit by a car) makes you think that the injury may be severe or that the child may have multiple injuries.

- It is not possible to safely or comfortably move the child to a vehicle for transport to a hospital.

20 minutes before applying the cold or ice pack again.

- **E** stands for **elevate.** Elevate the injured part only if it does not cause more pain. Elevating the injured part may help reduce swelling.

Splinting is a way to prevent movement of (immobilize) an injured bone or joint.

It can also help reduce pain. However, you should only apply a splint if you *must* move the child to get medical help and if splinting does not cause the child more pain or discomfort.

Splinting involves securing the injured body part to the splint to keep it from moving. There are many different things you can use to make a splint, including soft materials (like blankets, towels or pillows) or rigid materials (like a folded magazine or a board). You can even use part of the body as a splint (for example, you can splint an injured finger to the uninjured finger next to it, one leg to the other leg or an arm against the chest). This is called an anatomic splint.

Triangular bandages are handy to keep in your first aid kit in case you need to make a splint. A triangular bandage can be used to make a sling (a special kind of splint that is used to hold an injured arm against the chest) and to make ties to hold other kinds of splints in place. A "cravat fold" is used to turn a triangular bandage into a tie.

The general rules for applying a splint are the same no matter what type of splint you use:

- Splint the body part in the position in which you found it. Don't try to straighten or move the body part.

- Make sure the splint is long enough to extend above and below the injured area. If a joint is injured, include the bones above and below the joint in the splint. If a bone is injured, include the joints above and below the bone in the splint. If you aren't sure what is injured, include both the bones and the joints above and below the injured area in the splint.

- Check for feeling, warmth and color beyond the site of injury before and after splinting to make sure that the splint is not too tight.

For step-by-step instructions on making a soft splint, a rigid splint, an anatomic splint and a sling, see Skill Sheets 8-9 (Applying a Soft Splint), 8-10 (Applying a Rigid Splint), 8-11 (Applying an Anatomic Splint) and 8-12 (Applying a Sling) on pages 185-189.

Head, Neck and Spinal Injuries

Although head, neck and spinal injuries are only a small fraction of all injuries, they can be serious and even life threatening!

You should consider the possibility of a head, neck or spinal injury if the child:

- Was hit by a car, thrown from a moving car, or was in a car accident and was not properly secured in a child safety seat.

- Was injured entering shallow water, entering water from a significant height, or hitting his head on a diving board or waterslide.

- Is wearing a safety helmet that is now broken.

- Was injured as a result of a fall from a height greater than his own height.

- Says he has neck or back pain.

- Has an obvious head or neck injury.

- Says his arms or legs feel "tingly" or weak.

- Is not fully alert or unresponsive.

- Staggers when trying to walk.

- Appears to be weak.

If you suspect a head, neck or spinal injury, call 9-1-1 or the local emergency number immediately!

If you think that a child has a head, neck or spinal injury and she is conscious, ask her to respond verbally to any questions you ask. Tell her *not* to nod or shake her head!

Your goal in caring for a child with a head, neck or spinal injury is to minimize movement while you wait for emergency responders to arrive while trying to calm and reassure the child. If the child is breathing normally, gently support the child's head in the position you find it. Do this by placing your hands on both sides of the child's head in the position in which you found it. Support the child's head in this position until emergency responders arrive. If the head is turned sharply to one side, *do not* try to align it!

In addition to minimizing movement, also be sure to maintain an open airway and monitor breathing and changes in the child's condition.

DID YOU KNOW?

If the child with a suspected head, neck or spinal injury is wearing a helmet, do not remove it or any attached face masks or shields unless it is necessary to access and assess the child's airway and you are specifically trained to do so.

Concussion

A concussion is a temporary loss of brain function caused by a blow to the head. The effects of a concussion can appear immediately or soon after the blow to the head occurs.

Some effects of a concussion do not appear for hours or even days. These include sleep, mood and cognitive disturbances and sensitivity to light and noise.

Signals of a concussion may include:

- Confusion, which may last from moments to several minutes.

- Headache.

- Repeated questioning about what happened.

- Temporary memory loss, especially for periods immediately before and after the injury.

- Brief loss of consciousness.

- Nausea and vomiting.

- Speech problems (person is unable to answer questions or obey simple commands).

- Blurred vision or light sensitivity.

Treat every suspected concussion seriously. Call 9-1-1 or the local emergency number immediately! While you are waiting for emergency responders to arrive, support the head and neck in the position in which you found it, while making sure to maintain an open airway. Control any bleeding and apply dressings to any open wounds. However, do not apply direct pressure if there are signs of an obvious skull fracture. If there is clear liquid leaking from the ears or a wound in the scalp, cover the area loosely with gauze dressing. Monitor the child for any changes in condition, and try to calm and reassure the child. Encourage the child to engage in conversation with you (without moving his head or neck!) to prevent loss of consciousness.

DID YOU KNOW?

Sometimes the effects of a concussion do not appear for hours or even days. These delayed effects include sleep, mood and cognitive disturbances and sensitivity to light and noise.

DID YOU KNOW?

Most people with a concussion recover quickly and fully. But for some people, symptoms can last for days, weeks or longer. In general, recovery may be slower among young children, teens and older adults.

Skill Sheet 8-1: Assisting with an Asthma Inhaler

Note: *If possible, help the child to use the inhaler herself, instead of doing it for her.*

During the family interview, you should check the inhaler with the parents to ensure you can identify the right medication and understand how to use it.

1. Help the child sit up and lean slightly forward to make breathing easier.

2. Check the label on the inhaler to make sure it has the child's name on it and a description of the medication. Also check the expiration date on the inhaler.

   - If the medication does not have the child's name on it or is not intended for "quick relief" or "acute attacks," do not use it.

   - If the medication is expired, do not use it.

3. Shake the inhaler.

4. Remove the mouthpiece cover. If the child uses a spacer, attach it to the mouthpiece.

5. Ask the child to breathe out as much as possible through the mouth.

6. Help the child to take the medication.

   - **Spacer with mask.** Position the mask over the child's nose and mouth. Push the button on the top of the canister to release the medication into the spacer. Have the child breathe in and out normally about 5 or 6 times.

   - **Spacer.** Have the child close her lips tightly around the spacer. Push the button on the top of the canister to release the medication into the spacer. Have the child take a long, slow breath (about 3 to 5 seconds), and then hold his breath for a count of 10.

- **No spacer.** Position the mouthpiece of the inhaler according to the method the child uses. Some children may close their lips tightly around the mouthpiece of the inhaler. Others may hold the mouthpiece an inch or two away from the mouth (about two finger-widths). Have the child take a long, slow breath (about 3 to 5 seconds) while pressing down on the top of the canister. Then have the child hold his breath for a count of 10.

7. Note the time. The child's breathing should improve within 5 to 15 minutes. More than one dose of medication may be needed to stop the asthma attack. The label will tell you how long to wait between doses.

   - If the child's breathing does not improve or the child loses consciousness, call 9-1-1 or the local emergency number (if you haven't already).

8. Wash your hands.

Skill Sheet 8-2: Conscious Choking—Child (Older Than 1 Year)

1. Position yourself behind the child. Depending on the child's size, you may need to kneel.

2. Give **5** back blows.

   - Bend the child forward at the waist.

   - Firmly strike the child between the shoulder blades with the heel of your hand.

3. Give **5** abdominal thrusts.

   - Have the child stand up straight.

   - Find the child's belly button. Make a fist and place the thumb side against the child's stomach, right above the belly button.

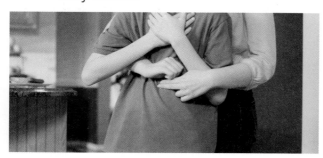

   - Cover the fist with your other hand.

   - Pull inward and upward to give an abdominal thrust.

4. Continue giving sets of **5** back blows and **5** abdominal thrusts until:

   - The object pops out of the child's mouth.

   - The child can cough forcefully, speak or breathe.

   - The child loses consciousness.

Note: *If the child loses consciousness, lower him to the floor and begin giving care for an unconscious choking child (see Skill Sheet 8-4), starting with 30 compressions.*

Skill Sheet 8-3: Conscious Choking—Infant

Note: *Always support the infant's head, neck and back while giving back blows and chest thrusts.*

1. Position the infant.

   - Place your forearm along the infant's back, cradling the back of her head with your hand.

   - Place your other forearm along the infant's front, holding her jaw with your thumb and fingers.

   - Turn the infant over so that she is face-down along your forearm.

   - Lower your arm onto your thigh so that the infant's head is lower than her chest.

2. Give **5** back blows.

   - Firmly strike the infant between the shoulder blades with the heel of your hand. Keep your fingers up so that you don't hit the infant's head or neck.

3. Reposition the infant.

   - Place one hand along the infant's back, cradling the back of her head with your hand.

   - While continuing to hold the infant's jaw with the thumb and fingers of your other hand, support her between your forearms and turn her over so that she is face-up along your forearm.

   - Lower your arm onto your other thigh so that the infant's head is lower than her chest.

4. Give **5** chest thrusts.

   - Place the pads of two or three fingers in the center of the infant's chest, on the breastbone. (To find the breastbone, imagine a line across the infant's chest that connects the nipples. Put your fingers just below this imaginary line, in the center of the chest.)

   - Press down about 1½ inches and then let the chest return to its normal position.

5. Continue giving sets of **5** back blows and **5** chest thrusts until:

   - The object pops out of the infant's mouth.

   - The infant can cough forcefully, cry or breathe.

   - The infant loses consciousness.

Note: *If the infant loses consciousness, place her on a hard, flat surface and begin giving care for an unconscious choking infant (see Skill Sheet 8-5), starting with 30 compressions.*

Skill Sheet 8-4: Unconscious Choking—Child (Older Than 1 Year)

Note: *Use disposable gloves and a breathing barrier to protect yourself from germs.*

1. Place the child on his back on a firm, flat surface. Kneel beside the child.

2. Give **30** chest compressions.

   - Place the heel of one hand in the center of the child's chest, with your other hand on top.

   - Lean forward so that your shoulders are directly over your hands.

   - Keeping your arms straight, push down about 2 inches, and then let the chest return to its normal position.

   - Push hard and push fast! Aim for a rate of 100 compressions per minute.

3. Open the child's mouth and look for the object.

   - Grasp the child's lower jaw between your thumb and forefinger, and open the mouth.

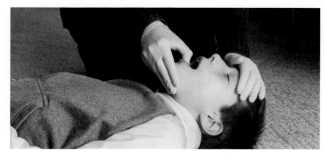

   - Look for the object.

   - If you see the object, remove it with your finger. If the child is small, use your pinky finger.

Note: *Never put your finger in the child's mouth unless you can actually see the object. If you can't see the object and you put your finger in the child's mouth, you might accidentally push*

the object deeper into the child's throat.

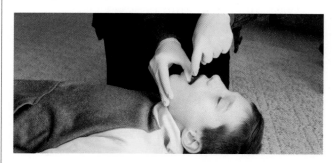

4. Try to give **2** rescue breaths.

   - Place the breathing barrier over the child's nose and mouth.

   - Open the airway. (Put one hand on the forehead and two fingers on the bony part of the chin, and tilt the head back until the chin is slightly further back than straight up-and-down.)

   - Pinch the nose shut and make a complete seal over the child's mouth with your mouth.

   - Take a normal breath and breathe into the child's mouth for about 1 second.

   - Release the seal and let the air out, and then try to give a second rescue breath.

Note: *If the breaths go in (that is, they make the chest clearly rise), remove the breathing barrier and check for breathing for no more than 10 seconds. Then give care according to the conditions that you find.*

5. Repeat steps 2 through 4 (compressions, check for object, rescue breaths) until:

   - The chest clearly rises on its own.

   - The child can cough, speak, cry or breathe on his own.

Skill Sheet 8-5: Unconscious Choking—Infant

Note: *Use disposable gloves and a breathing barrier to protect yourself from germs.*

1. Place the infant on his back on a firm, flat surface.

2. Give **30** chest compressions.

- Place two or three fingers on the center of the infant's chest, just below the nipple line.

- Place your other hand on the infant's forehead, and keep the head tilted back so that the chin is straight up-and-down.

- Keeping your fingers pointed down, push down about 1½ inches, and then let the chest return to its normal position.

- Push hard and push fast! Aim for a rate of 100 compressions per minute.

3. Open the infant's mouth and look for the object.

- Grasp the infant's lower jaw between your thumb and forefinger, and open the mouth.

- Look for the object.

- If you see the object, remove it with your pinky finger.

Note: *Never put your finger in the infant's mouth unless you can actually see the object. If you can't see the object and you put your finger in the infant's mouth, you might accidentally push the object deeper into the infant's throat.*

4. Try to give **2** rescue breaths.

- Place the breathing barrier over the infant's nose and mouth.

- Open the airway. (Put one hand on the forehead and two fingers on the bony part of the chin, and tilt the head back until the chin is straight up-and-down.)

- Make a complete seal over the infant's nose and mouth with your mouth.

- Take a normal breath, and breathe into the infant's nose and mouth for about 1 second.

- Release the seal and let the air out, and then give the second rescue breath.

Continued on next page

Skill Sheet 8-5: Unconscious Choking—Infant

(Continued)

Note: *If the breaths go in (that is, they make the chest clearly rise), remove the breathing barrier and check for breathing for no more than 10 seconds. Then give care according to the conditions that you find.*

5. Repeat steps 2 through 4 (compressions, check for object, rescue breaths) until:

    ■ The chest clearly rises on its own.

    ■ The infant can cough, cry or breathe on her own.

Skill Sheet 8-6: Taking a Temperature

1. Have the child sit or lie down. Make sure the child stays seated or lying down the entire time that you are taking the temperature.

2. If necessary, turn the thermometer on.

3. Take the temperature.

Axillary (Under the Arm) Temperature

- Uncover the underarm area and dry it with a tissue if necessary.

- Put the tip of the digital thermometer in the middle of the child's armpit, and then bring the child's arm across her chest to hold the thermometer in place.

- Keep the thermometer in place for 10 minutes or until the thermometer beeps.

Temporal (Across the Forehead) Temperature

- Place the sensor of the temporal thermometer at the center of the forehead, midway between the eyebrow and the hairline.

- Push the scan button and hold it down.

- Slowly slide the thermometer straight across the forehead toward the top of the ear, stopping when you reach the hairline. Make sure you keep contact with the skin.

- Release the scan button and remove the thermometer from the skin.

Tympanic (In the Ear) Temperature

Note: *If the child has just come in from being outside on a cold day, wait 15 minutes before taking the tympanic temperature.*

- Grasp the child's earlobe and pull *down and back* (in a child younger than 3 years) or grasp the top of the child's ear and pull *up and back* (in a child older than 3 years) to straighten the ear canal.

- Gently insert the probe of the tympanic thermometer into the ear, pointing it down and forward, toward the child's nose.

- When the thermometer beeps (usually in a few seconds), remove the probe from the ear.

Continued on next page

182

©2014 American Red Cross | Advanced Child Care Training

Skill Sheet 8-6: Taking a Temperature *(Continued)*

Oral (In the Mouth) Temperature

Note: *If the child has had a hot or cold drink in the last 15 minutes, wait 15 minutes before taking the oral temperature.*

- Put the tip of the digital thermometer under the child's tongue, toward the back and slightly to one side.

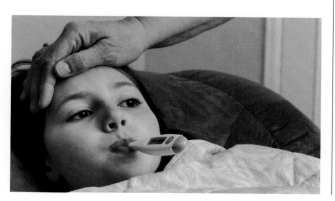

- Ask the child to close his lips around the thermometer. Remind him not to bite down on the thermometer with his teeth.

- Keep the thermometer in place for 5 to 8 minutes or until the thermometer beeps.

4. Read the number on the thermometer's display screen.

5. Follow the manufacturer's instructions for cleaning the thermometer.

6. Wash your hands.

Skill Sheet 8-7: Assisting with an Epinephrine Auto-Injector

Note: *During the family interview, you should check the auto-injector with the parents to ensure you can identify the right medication and understand how to use it. If possible, help the child to use the auto-injector on herself, instead of doing it for her. If the child is unconscious or unable to use the auto-injector on herself for some other reason, you may need to do it for her. Make sure to find out from the parents in advance if they want you to use the auto-injector to give medication to the child if the child is unable to give the medication to herself.*

1. Check the label on the auto-injector to make sure it has the child's name on it. Also check the expiration date on the auto-injector. If the medication is visible, check to make sure the medication is clear, not cloudy.

   - If the auto-injector does not have the child's name on it, do not use it.

   - If the medication is expired or cloudy, do not use it.

2. Determine whether the child has already given herself a dose of the medication. If she has, administer a second dose only if emergency responders are delayed and the child is still having signals of anaphylaxis.

3. Put on your disposable gloves.

4. Locate the outside middle of one thigh to use as the injection site.

   - Make sure there is nothing in the way, such as seams or items in a pocket.

5. Grasp the auto-injector firmly in your fist, and pull off the safety cap with your other hand.

6. Hold the tip of the auto-injector (the end with the needle) against the child's outer thigh so that the auto-injector is at a 90-degree angle to the thigh.

7. Quickly and firmly push the tip straight into the outer thigh. You will hear a click.

8. Hold the auto-injector firmly in place for 10 seconds, then remove it from the thigh and rub the injection site with your hand for several seconds.

9. Check the child's breathing and watch to see how she responds to the medication.

10. Place the used auto-injector in a cup or other hard plastic container with the tip facing down. Give it to the emergency responders when they arrive.

11. Remove your gloves and wash your hands.

Skill Sheet 8-8: Controlling Severe Bleeding

1. Put on your disposable gloves.

2. Cover the wound with a sterile gauze pad and apply direct pressure until the bleeding stops or slows.

- If blood soaks through the first gauze pad, put another one on top and continue to apply direct pressure.

3. Make a bandage by wrapping roll gauze around the wound several times to hold the gauze pads in place.

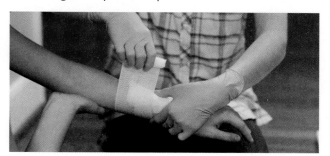

- Tie or tape the bandage to secure it.

- Check the skin on the side of the injury farthest away from the heart—the skin should be warm and its normal color, with normal feeling.

Note: *If the bleeding does not stop and blood soaks through the bandage, apply additional gauze pads and bandages on top of the first and continue to apply direct pressure. Call 9-1-1 or the local emergency number if you haven't already, and take steps to minimize shock.*

4. Remove your gloves and wash your hands.

Skill Sheet 8-9: Applying a Soft Splint

1. Choose a material to make your splint (for example, a folded blanket, towel or pillow). When wrapped around the injured area, it should be long enough to support the injured area above and below the site of the injury.

2. Check the skin beyond the injury for feeling, warmth and color.

   ■ Don't remove a shoe to check for warmth and color. Just check for feeling.

3. Fold several triangular bandages into ties and then place them under the injured body part, above and below the injured area.

4. Gently wrap the soft object you are using as a splint around the injured area.

5. Tie the triangular bandages securely around the splint to secure it.

   ■ Don't tie the bandages directly over the injury.

6. Recheck for feeling, warmth and color.

Skill Sheet 8-10: Applying a Rigid Splint

1. Choose a material to make your splint (for example, a folded magazine, a piece of cardboard or a board). When placed under the injured area, it should be long enough to support the injured area above and below the site of the injury.

2. Check the skin beyond the injury for feeling, warmth and color.

   ■ Don't remove a shoe to check for warmth and color. Just check for feeling.

3. Fold several triangular bandages into ties.

4. Place the splint under the injured body part.

   ■ If you are using something rough as a splint, like a board, wrap it in something soft to pad it and protect the skin.

   ■ If you are splinting an arm below the elbow, place a roll of gauze in the child's hand to keep the hand in a natural position.

5. Tie the triangular bandages securely around the splint to secure it.

   ■ Don't tie the bandages directly over the injury.

6. Recheck for feeling, warmth and color.

Skill Sheet 8-11: Applying an Anatomic Splint

1. Check the skin beyond the injury for feeling, warmth and color.

   - Don't remove a shoe to check for warmth and color. Just check for feeling.

2. Fold several triangular bandages into ties and then place them under the injured body part, above and below the injured area.

3. Place the uninjured body part next to the injured body part.

4. Tie the triangular bandages around the two body parts to secure them to each other.

   - Don't tie the bandages directly over the injury.

5. Recheck for feeling, warmth and color.

Skill Sheet 8-12: Applying a Sling

1. Check the skin beyond the injury for feeling, warmth and color.

2. Place a triangular bandage under the injured arm so that one point of the triangle is over the uninjured shoulder, one point is near the hand or elbow of the injured arm and one point hangs straight down.

3. Bring the point that is hanging straight down up over the injured shoulder and tie the ends of the sling at the side of the neck.

4. Fold a triangular bandage into a tie and use it to bind the injured arm to the chest.

5. Recheck for feeling, warmth and color.

ACTIVITY SHEETS

Getting to Know the Family—What Should You Ask?

Your instructor will assign you one or two topic areas to focus on. What questions would you ask the parents that relate to that topic area? Come up with as many as you can in 5 minutes.

Topic: Rules and Discipline

What should I do if she/she breaks the rules? (Consequences)
What rules do you have regarding play?
What rules do you have regarding electronics
Are there rules about what he/she eats?
Is your child known for breaking the rules
Are there any rules for me as the babysitter?
Normal household rules?

Topic:

FIND a Solution: Double Trouble

Use the FIND decision-making model to create a solution when you deal with a child who refuses to go to bed. Remember that FIND stands for:

- **F**: Figure out the problem.

- **I**: Identify possible solutions.

- **N**: Name the pros and cons for each solution.

- **D**: Decide which solution is best, then act on it.

Problem: Different bed times not wanting to go to bed

Solution 1: Hide and seek for 5 minutes

Pros: Both get to play

Cons: Riled up, not able to sleep

Solution 2: Get boy to help get girl to bed then play

Pros: The boy gets what he wants

Cons: The girl won't get to play

Solution 3: Have then chose a new calm activity out of options.

Pros: They would both get to do something they wanted

Cons: No hide and seek

Solution 4: Directive leadership

Pros: They'd to what you want

Cons: Possible tantrum, sad kids

Decision: Solution 3.

I.D. the Consequence

Read the description of each consequence, then decide which consequence each example describes. You may use a consequence more than once. Write in the answer below each situation.

Natural consequences are the natural results of a child's action.

Logical consequences are those that are closely related to an action.

Withholding privileges means not allowing the child to do something he enjoys. This is usually used on preschoolers and school-age children.

A time-out is a consequence that involves removing the child from the situation and putting him or her in a quiet, easily seen place for a brief amount of time, usually 1 minute for each year of age. This is usually used on older toddlers and preschoolers.

1. Jenny continues to tease her brother, so you have her sit in the corner for 4 minutes. *Time out*

2. You tell Amy that if she continues to play with her Popsicle, it might fall on the floor and she won't be able to eat it. *Natural*

3. Robby knocks over his little brother's sand castle, so you tell Robby he must help him build another one. *Logical*

4. David wouldn't stop playing video games to brush his teeth after lunch, so now he is not allowed to play video games for the rest of the evening. *Withholding privileges*

5. Emily would not stop eating the chocolate in the candy dish, so she does not get to have dessert for dinner. *Logical*

6. You tell Jeremy that if he does not finish his chores, he cannot go to the pool. *Withholding privileges*

FIND a Solution: Little Picasso

Use the FIND decision-making model to create a solution when you discover a child has drawn on the walls. Remember that FIND stands for:

- **F**: Figure out the problem.

- **I**: Identify possible solutions.

- **N**: Name the pros and cons for each solution.

- **D**: Decide which solution is best, then act on it.

Problem:

Solution 1:

Pros:

Cons:

Solution 2:

Pros:

Cons:

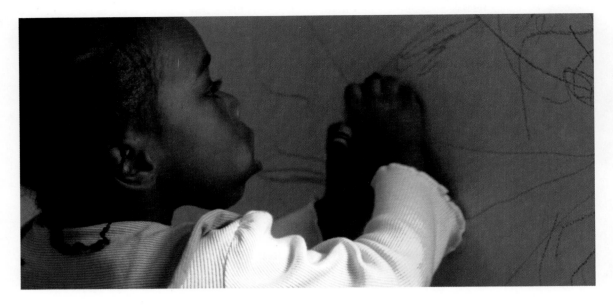

Solution 3:

Pros:

Cons:

Decision:

Creating Developmentally Appropriate Play

Using the table Understanding Kids of All Ages: Keeping Kids Entertained in Chapter 4 of your Handbook, come up with at least one play activity per element listed in your instructor-assigned developmental stage.

Developmental Stage: _Pre-Schooler_

Paper: ~~Paper~~
Paper Airplanes
Trash Ket Ball

Five Senses: Make Believe
I Spy
Reading Using touch

Household Items: Spoon Catapult
Silverware band
How things with straws

FIND a Solution: But My Parents Let Me!

Use the FIND decision-making model to create a solution when you discover a child has drawn on the walls. Remember that FIND stands for:

- **F**: Figure out the problem.

- **I**: Identify possible solutions.

- **N**: Name the pros and cons for each solution.

- **D**: Decide which solution is best, then act on it.

Problem:

Solution 1:

Pros:

Cons:

Solution 2:

Pros:

Cons:

Solution 3:

Pros:

Cons:

Decision:

MEMORY CHALLENGE–Diapering

You worked through a diapering scenario in the online portion of the course. Read each question, then fill in the answer based on what you learned in the scenario.

> **Scenario Review:**
>
> Charlotte wakes up from her late-morning nap and is crying in her crib. You pick her up and realize that it is time for a diaper change.

1. In this scenario, you learned that it was better to put Charlotte back in her crib while you washed your hands and gathered supplies than to put her on the changing table and secure her with safety straps. Why was this the better move?

2. When wiping, what did you learn was the method that best minimizes the spread of bacteria and chance for infection?

3. In this scenario, you learned that if you see the signs of diaper rash (red, irritated skin), it is best to expose the area to air for a few minutes before putting a new diaper on, instead of using diaper rash cream or baby powder. Why is this the recommended method over a topical product?

TEAM CHALLENGE—Everyday Child Care

Follow each question one at a time along with the instructor. Deliberate with your team and come up with the answers as fast as possible. First team representative to raise his or her hand and provide the correct answer wins the points!

1. **Topic: Putting Baby to Bed**
   In the nursery, you clicked on the night-light, which gave you tips on putting a child down for bedtime.

   ○ How many minutes in advance should you tell a child that bedtime is approaching?

   ○ How often is it recommended that you check on a sleeping child?

2. **Topic: Potty Help**
   In the bathroom, you clicked on the toilet, which gave you tips on helping toddlers use the potty.

   ○ There are three everyday activities before and after which you should ask a child whether they want to use the potty. Name all three of those everyday activities.

3. **Topic: Meal Planning**
   In the kitchen, you clicked on the cookbook for tips on meals.
   Match the correct age group with the correct fact.

1. Younger than 6 months	_____	**A.** Must be encouraged to drink from a cup and are known to be picky eaters.
2. Age 6–8 months	_____	**B.** Should be offered calcium-based and protein-based snacks, like cheese and hard-cooked eggs.
3. Age 9–12 months	_____	**C.** Should be encouraged to choose nutritious snacks with a focus on iron and protein.
4. Toddlers	_____	**D.** Feedings of breast milk or formula are typical. Cereal becomes a supplemental food.
5. Preschoolers	_____	**E.** Tries using a spoon and is introduced to small finger foods.
6. School-age Child	_____	**F.** Apple and noncitrus juices and solid foods, like strained fruits and veggies, are introduced.

4. **Topic: Crying Baby**

   In the nursery, you clicked on the crib for tips on handling a baby who is crying.

   o   If a baby starts to cry, there are five basic questions you should ask yourself to try and figure out what is wrong. List three of those questions.

5. **Topic: Hygiene Basics**

   In the bathroom, you clicked on the tub and the sink for tips on bathing children and helping children brush their teeth.

   o   You learned that you don't need to fill the bathtub very high to bathe a child. The water only needs to come up to the child's what?

   o   Children up to 7 years old will need help brushing their teeth. You should help them brush for how long?

6. **Topic: Morning Routines with School-Aged Child**

   In the bedroom, you clicked on the bed for tips on morning routines for a school-aged child.

   o   There are several tips to ensure that a morning runs smoothly before a child goes to school. Name one thing you can do.

Activity is complete! Tally up the scores.

AED—Fact or Fiction

Read each statement about AEDs. Do you think the statement is Fact or Fiction? Write in your answers below.

1. AED pads must be removed before performing CPR. **Fact** or **fiction**?

2. If the placement of the AED pads is reversed, the AED will not work. **Fact** or **fiction**?

3. It is safe to use an AED in rain or snow. **Fact** or **fiction**?

4. If a person has a body piercing or is wearing jewelry, you should remove the item before using an AED. **Fact** or **fiction**?

5. Never shock a person on a metal surface. **Fact** or **fiction**?

Test Your Instincts

Read each statement or question about sudden illnesses, and answer to the best of your knowledge and instincts.

1. Constipation is a common signal of sudden illness.

   A) True

   B) False

2. You don't need to know exactly what is wrong to provide care to a child or infant who is suddenly ill.

   A) True

   B) False

3. A child with diabetes can become ill if there is:

   A) Too much sugar in his blood.

   B) Too little sugar in his blood.

   C) Either situation might trigger a diabetic emergency.

4. A child who is having a diabetic emergency may act abnormally or feel confused.

   A) True

   B) False

5. If a child is having a diabetic emergency, which of the following is a good thing to give him?

   A) A glass of water.

   B) A can of a sugary soft drink.

   C) You shouldn't give him anything. Call 9-1-1 right away.

6. If a child exposed to an allergen breaks out in hives, it is a signal that the reaction is:

   A) Mild.

   B) Severe.

   C) Neither. Hives are not a signal of an allergic reaction.

7. Having an allergic reaction means the person has anaphylaxis, a life-threatening condition.

   A) True

   B) False

8. If a child with a known allergy carries an epinephrine auto-injector, you should let him inject himself if he can.

A) True

B) False

9. The temperature at which a child is considered to have a fever is:

A) 100.4° F.

B) 100.5° F.

C) 100.6° F.

10. After a child vomits, it is recommended that you lay her:

A) On her back.

B) On her side.

C) Neither; sitting her up is best.

11. When a child has diarrhea, you should reintroduce foods:

A) After a few hours.

B) When the child says she is hungry.

C) Either may be OK, but you should call the parents first and follow their care instructions.

12. Exercise can trigger an asthma attack.

A) True

B) False

13. A child who is having an asthma attack should:

A) Sit down.

B) Stand up.

C) Stay in any position that is comfortable to him.

14. When a child takes his asthma medication, you will likely see improvement in breathing within:

A) 1 to 2 minutes.

B) 5 to 15 minutes.

C) 20 to 30 minutes.

MEMORY CHALLENGE— Allergic Reaction

You worked through an allergy scenario in the online portion of the course. Read each question, then fill in the answer based on what you learned in the scenario.

Scenario Review:

You were watching Jackson and Sadie during a school holiday. Sadie has a severe tree nut allergy and mild egg allergies, and you were tasked with serving her lunch.

---

1. In this scenario, what would have been the best way to prepare yourself to care for Sadie's allergies ahead of time?

2. You had a choice of three foods to offer Sadie: apple slices with peanut butter, a packaged granola bar, or carrot sticks with ranch dressing. Which of these would not have triggered an allergic reaction in Sadie?

3. In this scenario, some of you went down a path where Sadie had a mild reaction to the ranch dressing, while others went down a path where Sadie had a severe reaction to the granola bar. For either situation, what was the first thing you needed to do before providing care?

MEMORY CHALLENGE–External Bleeding

You worked through a bleeding scenario in the online portion of the course. Read each question, then fill in the answer based on what you learned in the scenario.

Scenario Review:

While playing with Reva and Ishan on a swing set, Reva slipped off the ladder and sustained a deep cut on her shin.

---

1. In this scenario, Reva's shin was bleeding and you needed to apply pressure to her wound with a sterile dressing to try and stop the bleeding. Was the appropriate amount of pressure firm or gentle?

2. Reva was bleeding through the gauze. What did you learn was the appropriate way to address this problem?

3. How many minutes went by before you called 9-1-1 because Reva's bleeding could not be slowed or stopped?

Dazed and Confused

Look at each photo and read and answer the corresponding questions.

Image 1 *Maggie is caring for Martha. It is a beautiful day, so Maggie takes Martha to the park. Martha is climbing around on the playground equipment. Sensing something has just happened, Maggie turns around and notices Martha clumsily getting back on her feet after an apparent fall. As Maggie walks towards Martha, she seems disoriented and off-balance.*

1. What are the signals of an injury here?

2. What may have happened?

3. What kind of injury could this be?

Image 2 *Martha has stumbled on her way to sit down. She continues to look confused. Maggie, who is trained in first aid, begins to offer assistance.*

4. What do you see happening in this photo?

5. Why is the responder positioned the way she is?

6. What care steps should the responder be following?

SAMPLE FORMS FOR CAREGIVERS

Sample Résumé

Rachel Smith

1204 Street Lane
New York, NY 11202

555-123-0123
rsmith92@email.com

EDUCATION

State University–Class of 2014

Early Childhood Education, B.A.

TRAINING

American Red Cross Advanced Child Care Training

Leadership, professionalism, safety, child development, basic child care and emergency care

ADDITIONAL TRAINING

American Red Cross First Aid

American Red Cross CPR–Child and Infant

CAREGIVING EXPERIENCE

The Shah Family   July 6 to August 14, 2014
Worked three nights each week caring for two school-age children

The Kim Family   March 30 to June 12, 2014
Provided care for an infant, including bottle-feeding, diapering, dressing and more

OTHER EXPERIENCE

Volunteered at homeless shelter and tutored children while in college

Worked safely with children as an American Red Cross Lifeguard and Water Safety Instructor

SKILLS AND ABILITIES

Patient and child-friendly personality, proficient in creative arts and crafts and excellent tutoring skills

HOBBIES

Arts and crafts, photography and volunteering

REFERENCES

Daniel Kim	(555)-444-3333	Former client
Kevin Shah	(555)-443-0283	Former client
John Mears	(555)-321-9043	Former professor

Sample Business Card

Child Care 1-2-3

Rachel Smith
1204 Street Lane
New York, NY 11201
555-123-0123   rsmith92@gmail.com

Caregiving Services

Caregiver's Self-Assessment Tool

Answer these questions to discover your skills, abilities, likes and dislikes about caregiving. There is no right or wrong answer. Update the Caregiver's Self-Assessment Tool every 6 months.

Background and Experience

1. The number of caregiving jobs I have had is:

    ☐ None   ☐ 1–3   ☑ 4–6   ☐ 7–10   ☐ More than 10

2. The most children I have cared for at one time is:

    ☐ 1   ☑ 2   ☐ 3   ☐ 4   ☐ 5 or more

3. The youngest child I have ever cared for is a(n):

    ☑ Infant (newborn to 12 months)

    ☐ Toddler (1 and 2 years)

    ☐ Preschooler (3 and 4 years)

    ☐ Younger school-age child (5, 6 and 7 years)

    ☐ Older school-age child (8, 9 and 10 years)

4. The oldest child I have ever cared for is a(n):

    ☐ Infant (newborn to 12 months)

    ☐ Toddler (1 and 2 years)

    ☐ Preschooler (3 and 4 years)

    ☐ Younger school-age child (5, 6 and 7 years)

    ☑ Older school-age child (8 years and older)

5. My longest caregiving job lasted:

    ☐ 1-3 hours   ☐ 4-5 hours   ☐ 6-8 hours   ☑ 8 or more hours

6. I have accepted caregiving jobs (check all that apply):

    ☑ On weekdays   ☑ On weeknights

    ☑ On weekend days   ☑ On weekend nights

    ☑ During vacation times   ☐ During the school year

Special Skills and Abilities

7. My special abilities include (check all that apply):

☐ Music ☑ Patience ☑ Like kids ☑ Arts and crafts ☑ Creativity

☐ Sports ☑ Good student ☐ Storytelling ☐ Sense of humor

☑ Other: __Cooking__

8. My leadership and caregiving skills include (rate your ability):

Making good decisions

☐ Needs work ☑ Good ☐ Very good

Problem solving

☐ Needs work ☐ Good ☑ Very good

Staying calm in an emergency

☐ Needs work ☑ Good ☐ Very good

Communicating well with children

☐ Needs work ☑ Good ☐ Very good

Modeling positive behavior

☐ Needs work ☐ Good ☑ Very good

Recognizing and respecting differences among children and families

☐ Needs work ☐ Good ☑ Very good

Correcting misbehavior appropriately

☐ Needs work ☑ Good ☐ Very good

Recognizing and making considerations for the developmental stages of children
at different ages

☐ Needs work ☑ Good ☐ Very good

Assessing caregiving jobs and gathering the necessary information before starting the job

☐ Needs work ☑ Good ☐ Very good

Acting professionally at all times

☐ Needs work ☐ Good ☑ Very good

9. My safety and first aid skills include (rate your ability):

Recognizing and removing or limiting safety-related problems

☐ Needs work   ☑ Good   ☐ Very good

Supervising children at all times

☐ Needs work   ☐ Good   ☑ Very good

Choosing appropriate toys and activities for children of different ages

☐ Needs work   ☐ Good   ☑ Very good

Recognizing and acting promptly in an emergency

☐ Needs work   ☐ Good   ☑ Very good

Giving appropriate care for children of different ages

☐ Needs work   ☐ Good   ☑ Very good

Check all that apply:

☑ Being certified in American Red Cross CPR–Child and Infant

☑ Being certified in American Red Cross Standard First Aid

10. My basic child care skills include (rate your ability):

Diapering

☐ Needs work   ☑ Good   ☐ Very good

Feeding children with a bottle or a spoon

☐ Needs work   ☑ Good   ☐ Very good

Helping children get rest and sleep

☑ Needs work   ☐ Good   ☐ Very good

Picking up and holding children correctly

☐ Needs work   ☑ Good   ☐ Very good

Giving appropriate care for children of different ages

☐ Needs work   ☑ Good   ☐ Very good

Preferences

11. I prefer to care for (check all that apply):

☐ One child at a time

☑ Infants

☑ Toddlers

☑ Preschoolers

☐ School-age children

12. The time of day I can provide care is:

☐ Mornings   ☑ Afternoons

☑ Evenings   ☐ Nights

13. I absolutely do NOT want to provide care when:

I will be caring for more than four children.

Parental Consent and Contact Form

This form is to be completed and signed by the child's parent or legal guardian.

The signature of the parent or legal guardian indicates permission for the caregiver to follow and act in accordance with these instructions. Use a separate form for each child.

Name of child: __Sadie Young__

Age: __7__

Weight: __72 lbs.__

Date of birth: __February 1st, 2007__

Medical condition(s) of concern:

Severe allergy to tree nuts; mild allergy to eggs

Allergies to medications:

None

Signal(s) to watch for:

A mild reaction: Skin irritation, hives, itching, nausea, upset stomach
A severe reaction: Trouble breathing; a rash and/or unusual swelling; tightness in the chest and throat; swelling of the face, neck or tongue; dizziness or confusion; and signs of shock (skin is cool, pale and sweaty)

List the child's prescription and over-the-counter medications. Be sure to include all medications; this will assist emergency medical services (EMS) personnel in the event of an emergency.

	Dose	How Given	When Given	Special Instructions (e.g., to be taken with water or food)	Possible Side Effects
Medication: Epinephrine	.01 mg	Auto-injector	Administer during a severe allergic reaction.	- Remove cap. - Inject needle into side of thigh. - Hold auto-injector against thigh for 10 seconds. - Remove needle and dispose properly.	None
Medication: Antihistamine	One tablet	Orally	During a mild allergic reaction	None	None
Medication:					

I give permission for ___Rachel Smith___ (Caregiver) to administer medicine(s) to
___Sadie Young___ (Child) in the manner described and to give basic first aid
to the child named above and take the appropriate action including contacting
emergency medical services (EMS) personnel. I give my permission to the Caregiver
to contact EMS personnel and arrange for transportation to ___St. Ellen's___ or the
nearest appropriate medical facility to receive the appropriate level of care as determined
by qualified medical professionals. Further, I give permission to the appropriate medical
facility to treat my child in the event of an emergency. In the event the child named above
is injured or ill, I understand that the Caregiver will attempt to contact me, the other parent
or legal guardian or the person I have designated to make decisions if I cannot be reached
using the contact numbers listed below.

Contact Numbers ___(555) 320-3450___ on ___Anytime___ (hours/days)

_____ on _____ (hours/days)

_____ on _____ (hours/days)

Parent's/Legal guardian's name: ___Teresa Young___

Name and phone number of an adult who can make decisions if the parent
cannot be reached: ___Ruth Young___

Contact Numbers ___(555) 329-2390___ on ___Anytime___ (hours/days)

_____ on _____ (hours/days)

_____ on _____ (hours/days)

_____ _____

Parent/Legal guardian signature _____

Date _____

Family Interview Form
Family Information and Emergency Numbers

Today's date: __June 24th__

Family name: __Shah__

Home phone number: __(555) 343-0283__

Address: __119 George Street__

E-mail address: __kshah@email.com__

Nearest cross street: __Jefferson Avenue__

Phone number where parent can be reached during caregiving job: __(555) 012-8941__

Child's name	Age	Weight	Medicines	Allergies	Medical problems
Ishan	10	91 lbs.	- Quick relief inhaler as needed - Daily-use inhaler	None	Allergies
Reva	8	67 lbs.	None	None	None

Mobile phone number: __(555) 395-4928__

Neighbor's name and phone number: __Mrs. Ngo – (555) 374-2395__

Name and phone number of an adult who can make decisions if the parent cannot be reached:

__Leslie Chopra – Aunt (555) 694-2741__

Local emergency phone number: __9-1-1__

Doctor's name: __Dr. James__

Doctor's phone number: __(555) 723-1224__

Name of preferred hospital to be used in an emergency: __Jefferson Ave. Medical Center__

National Poison Control Center (PCC) hotline: (800) 222-1222

Household Rules and Discipline

1. What are the household rules?

   - No wrestling or rough play.

   - No shouting inside.

2. How would you like me to handle misbehavior?

   If the children are fighting, give them a chance to work it out on their own. If one of them is in danger of getting hurt, intervene and separate them.

3. Do the children need to complete any homework or chores? If so, when should the children complete their homework or chores? Will they need assistance?

   They will both have homework on days after school. Make sure all homework is completed before they begin any play activities.

Safety and Play

1. Would you take me on a tour of your house?
   Completed.

2. I would like to go over the **Caregiver's Safety Inspection Checklist** with you. Is that OK?

   Reviewed.

3. Does your family have a fire escape plan? If not, can you have one in place before I begin?

   Fire escape plan is posted on the refrigerator.

4. Do your children know what to do in a fire emergency?

   Ishan and Reva know to leave through the closest door when the smoke alarm goes off.

NOTE: *Families can find out more about how to be prepared for fires and other emergencies by contacting their local American Red Cross chapter or visiting redcross.org/disaster/masters.*

5. Does your house have working smoke alarms? Carbon monoxide alarm?

   Fire extinguisher? Where is the shut-off valve for water, electricity and gas?

   All of the alarms and fire extinguishers are up-to-date and working properly. The shut-off valve is in the hall closet.

6. Is it OK to take the children outside to play?
    Yes, but make sure they stay in the yard and out of the street.

7. Should I apply insect repellent or sunscreen to the children before they play outside?

    If so, what insect repellent or sunscreen should I use? Do any of the children have

    allergies or sensitivities to any of them?
    Have both kids use sunscreen and insect repellant before going outside. The
    preferred bottles will be on the kitchen table. Reapply sunscreen after swimming.

8. Do you have any pets that I need to care for? Are they friendly to strangers?
    Ishan has a goldfish, but I won't need to take care of it.

9. May I meet your children (and pets) before I care for them?
    I have known the children for 2 years.

10. What are your family's rules for play? What are your family's rules for watching TV,

    using the computer and playing video games?
    Ishan and Reva are limited to one hour of recreational screen time per day.
    However, homework must be completed before this can happen.

11. What are your children's favorite toys and play activities?
    Ishan and Reva both like to build towers and cities with Ishan's Connect-Os.

12. Are there any play areas, toys or activities that are off-limits or restricted?
    Do not allow the children to play in our bedroom, the kitchen, or the bathrooms.

13. How do I work the door and window locks?

    Demonstrated during house tour.

14. Do you have an electronic security system? Would you like me to use it and can you
    please show me how it works? What should I do if it is mistakenly set off?

    Yes. Demonstrated during tour. The alarm company will automatically call Mr. Shah.
    I should call Mr. Shah to let him know it was an accident.

15. Where is your first aid kit kept?
    In the medicine cabinet in the bathroom.

16. Where is your emergency preparedness kit kept?
    In the hall closet.

NOTE: *Families can find out more about how to prepare for emergencies by contacting their local American Red Cross chapter or visiting* redcross.org/disaster/masters.

17. Is there a spare house key for me to use?
    Yes. It will be left on the table.

Basic Child Care

1. How do you want me to handle hand washing?
   Both children are old enough to wash their own hands. Make sure they do so after using the bathroom or playing outside.

2. How do you want me to handle brushing and flossing teeth?

   Both children are old enough to brush their own teeth. Make sure they do so before bed.

3. What can your children eat and drink? Do they have any food allergies?

   Neither of the children have any food allergies. They can eat whatever food is in the refrigerator or pantry.

4. Will I be preparing any simple meals?
   I may need to make lunch for them.

5. What are the routines for diapering and/or using the toilet? Where are baby wipes and cleaning materials kept? Where do you want me to put dirty diapers and soiled disposable gloves?
   Ishan and Reva will use the toilet when they need to. They can do this themselves.

6. What are the routines for quiet time, bedtime and naps? When is bedtime? Do your children have a favorite bedtime story? Do they like a light on? Do you prefer their door open or closed? Do they sleep with particular blankets or stuffed animals?

Both children go to bed at 9:00 p.m. They both read quietly before bed. Ishan likes his door closed, and Reva likes hers open. They both sleep with nightlights.

7. What do you want your children to wear for outdoor play? For naptime? For bedtime?

They can wear normal clothes for outdoor play. They must wear bathing suits in the pool. Make sure they sleep in their pajamas.

8. Where do I put dirty clothing?

Make sure Ishan and Reva put their dirty clothes in the hamper in the hall.

9. Would you please show me any special equipment I might be using to take care of the children? No special equipment.

10. Are there any medical conditions or medications that I should be aware of? If the child is taking medication, where is it kept? Would you please fill out this **Parental Consent and Contact Form**? Does your child have an AAP Emergency Information Form for Children With Special Health Care Needs? Would you provide a copy that I can give to EMS and/or hospital personnel in case of an emergency? Are there special instructions or precautions I should be aware of?

Ishan has asthma. If he has an asthma attack, please help him use his quick relief inhaler and call 9-1-1.

NOTE: *If the parents do not fill out the **Parental Consent and Contact Form**, you should not give the children any medications.*

11. Do your children have any other specific care needs or routines that I should know about (for example, tutoring, music or sports practice, faith practices)?

No.

12. Do the children attend school or other activities outside of the home? What are the routines and schedules? Do I need to transport them?

Ishan and Reva both attend Brookside Elementary School, but they'll be home by the time the job begins each day.

13. Do your pets need any special care?

No pets.

14. Is there anything else I need to be aware of?

Both kids are proficient swimmers, but they need to be supervised when in the pool. Horseplay is not allowed, and the pool gates must be closed at all times.

Business Basics

1. What is the date and beginning and ending time of the job?

5:00 p.m. – 10:00 p.m. on Mondays, Wednesdays and Thursdays, starting July 6th.

2. Should I answer the phone? If so, how should I do so?

Answer the phone and take a message, if there is one.

3. Are there any rules I should observe in your home? May I use the TV, radio or computer?

Once the children are asleep, I can watch TV.

4. May I make a short personal call? May I do schoolwork once the children are asleep? May I fix a snack?

I can use the phone if I need to and help myself to food in the pantry.

5. I usually charge $ 14 for my hourly rate. Is that OK?

Family Emergency Information Card

Call 9-1-1 or the local emergency number, _____, in an emergency.

Family name:

Parent name:

1. Daniel Kim

2. Joan Kim

Phone number:

Parent 1: (555) 444-3333

Parent 2: (555) 444-3132

Mobile phone number:

Parent 1: (555) 426-3042

Parent 2: (555) 444-5454

Address: 1622 Brown Ave

E-mail address:

Parent 1: dkim@email.com

Parent 2: jakim@email.com

Child information

Name, age, weight, and hair and eye color

1. Charlotte, 4 months, 16 lbs,
   black hair, brown eyes.

2. _____

3. _____

Allergies:
None

Medications:
None

Medical problems:
None

Doctor's name:
Dr. Martinez

Nearest cross street:

Broad Street

Phone number and name of place where parent or guardian can be reached during caregiving job:

(555) 444-5454

Neighbor's name and phone number: Name and phone number of an adult who can make decisions if the parent cannot be reached:

Miss Shelley, (555) 444-5454

Doctor's phone number:

(555) 589-1288

Name of preferred hospital to be used in an emergency:

St. Jacob's Hospital

Poison Control Center (PCC) Hotline:

800-222-1222

Evacuation location:

Intersection of Brown Avenue and Broad Street

Emergency contact:

Daniel Kim

(555) 444-3333

Out-of-town contact information

Name: Allen Kim

Daytime phone: (555) 121-8475

Mobile phone: (555) 113-0984

E-mail: aekim22@email.com

Caregiver's Report Record

Household Rules and Discipline

a. I noticed these good behaviors:

Ishan and Reva played nicely together on the swing set.

Ishan helped clean up after dinner

b. I encountered the following behavior challenges:

What the Child Did/Did Not Do	What I Did
Ishan and Reva fought over the Connect-Os.	I allowed them to work out a solution on their own.

Safety

a. We received the following phone calls and visitors:

Date/Time	Name	Reason for Calling or Visiting	Visitor's Phone Number
July 10th, 6:30 p.m.	Jake Lawrence	Dinner plans this weekend	(555)-520-0325
July 13th, 7:15 p.m.	Lauren Williams	Sales call	(555)-932-3278

b. The following accidents and illnesses happened while you were gone:

Date/Time	What Happened	Where It Took Place	What I Did	What the Child Did
July 10th, 7:00 p.m.	Reva cut her leg playing outside	Near the swing set	Provided first aid care	Cried and said her leg hurt

Play

a. We played with the following games and toys:

We swam in the pool, then Ishan and Reva played with Ishan's Connect-Os.

Later, they played on the swing set.

b. I noticed these good behaviors while we were playing:

Ishan and Reva played very nicely together. They were safe

and kind to each other in the pool.

Basic Care

a. We ate the following foods:

Turkey sandwiches, potato chips and watermelon

b. Ishan _____ (child's name) had naptime/went to bed

at 9:00 p.m. (time). Ishan (child's name) slept for 1 hour (hours/minutes)

and woke up _____ times.

Reva _____ (child's name) had naptime/went to bed

at 9:00 p.m. (time). Reva (child's name) slept for 1 hour (hours/minutes)

and woke up _____ times.

c. For _____ (child's name), I changed the diaper/helped

with toileting _____ times.

For _____ (child's name), I changed the diaper/helped

with toileting _____ times.

Other Comments

Tonight was a very pleasant caregiving experience.

_____

I gave N/A _____ (child's name) the following medications and

amounts exactly as instructed by N/A _____ (parent or guardian):

Time: N/A   Medicine: N/A

Amount given: N/A

Any reactions: N/A

Caregiver's Safety Inspection Checklist

For Emergencies

☑ The emergency phone list has been filled out and is posted.

☑ The first aid kit is properly stocked and stored away.

☑ I know where the working flashlights, battery-operated radio and extra batteries are located.

To Prevent Wounds

☑ Knives, hand tools, power tools, razor blades, scissors, guns, ammunition and other objects that can cause injury are stored in locked cabinets or locked storage areas.

To Prevent Falls

☐ Safety gates are installed at all open stairways when taking care of small children and infants.

☑ Windows and balcony doors have childproof latches or window guards.

☐ Balconies have protective barriers to prevent children from slipping through the bars.

☑ The home is free of clutter on the floors, especially on or near stairways.

To Prevent Poisoning

☑ Potential poisons, like detergents, polishes, pesticides, car-care fluids, lighter fluids and lamp oils, are stored in locked cabinets and are out of reach of children.

☑ Houseplants are kept out of reach.

☑ Medicine is kept in a locked storage place that children can't reach.

☑ Child-resistant packaging is closed or reclosed securely.

To Prevent Burns

☑ Safety covers are placed on all unused electrical outlets.

☑ Loose cords are secured and out of the way. Multi-cord or octopus plugs are not used.

☑ At least one approved smoke alarm is installed and operating on each level of the home.

☐ Space heaters are placed out of reach of children and away from curtains.

☑ Flammable liquids are securely stored in their original containers and away from heat.

☑ Matches and lighters are stored out of reach of children.

☑ Garbage and recycling materials are stored in covered containers.

To Prevent Drowning

☐ Swimming pools and hot tubs are completely enclosed with a barrier, such as a locked fence, gate and cover.

☑ Wading pools and bathtubs are emptied when not in use.

☑ Toilet seats and lids are kept down when not in use.

☑ Bathroom doors are kept closed at all times.

☑ Buckets or other containers with standing water are securely covered or emptied of water.

To Prevent Choking and Other Breathing Dangers

☑ Small objects are kept out of children's reach.

☑ The toy box has ventilation holes. If there is a lid, it is a lightweight removable lid, a sliding door or panel or a hinged lid with a support to hold it open.

☐ The crib mattress fits the side of the crib snugly and toys, blankets and pillows are removed from the crib.

☑ Drape and blind cords are wound up and not dangling.

FUN ACTIVITIES
FOR KIDS

Activity: Coffee Filter Butterflies!

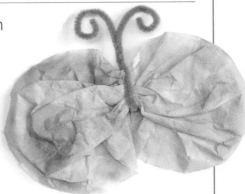

Appropriate For: Preschoolers and school-age children

WHAT YOU NEED:

- Large coffee filters
- Water-based markers or watercolor paint and brushes
- Pipe cleaners in assorted colors
- Small spray bottle filled with water

WHAT YOU DO:

Give the child a coffee filter and have him color on it with markers or paint on it with the watercolor paint. Encourage the child to make designs and to use lots of different colors. Have the child hold up the coffee filter, while you spray it with water. Let the child watch the colors spread and run together. When the filter is dry, gather it together in the middle and wrap a pipe cleaner around it, so that the two ends of the pipe cleaner stick up at the top. Curl the two ends of the pipe cleaner to make the butterfly's antennae.

Activity: Fancy Fruit Parfaits

Appropriate For: Preschoolers and school-age children

WHAT YOU NEED:

- 1 cup vanilla yogurt
- ¼ cup sliced strawberries
- ¼ cup blueberries
- 3 tablespoons granola

- Fancy parfait glass or clear plastic cup

WHAT YOU DO:

Have the child spoon some yogurt into the glass, and then top the yogurt with some fruit and some granola. Continue making layers, alternating between yogurt, fruit and granola, until the glass or cup is full, ending with a layer of fruit and granola. Enjoy! Makes 1 serving.

NOTES:

- Check with the parents before making and serving this recipe. Some children may have food allergies or other dietary restrictions.
- Any fruit that is available and in season and that the child likes can be substituted for the strawberries and blueberries.

Activity: Follow the Leader

Appropriate For: Toddlers and up with increasing difficulty for older children

WHAT YOU NEED:

- Your imagination
- Space to move around freely

WHAT YOU DO:

Have the child follow your lead as you travel. Every 30 seconds or so, change the activity. You can also let the child lead and you follow. Here are some suggestions for activities:

- Walk with giant steps and big swinging arms.
- Jump up and down in place.
- Hop like a bunny.
- Squat and walk like a duck.
- Twirl around in circles.

- Touch your toes.
- Do scissor jumps (cross legs with one jump, uncross legs on the next jump).

Activity: H.O.R.S.E.

Appropriate For: school-age children

WHAT YOU NEED:

- Basketball
- Basketball hoop

WHAT YOU DO:

Choose the order in which the players will shoot at the basket. The first player makes any kind of shot at the hoop. If the first player fails to make the shot, she loses her position as the leader and the next player in line becomes the leader. However, if the first player makes the shot, the other players get one chance to try to make the same shot (from the same place, using the same style). Any player who fails to do so gets an "H" (as in H.O.R.S.E, the name of the game).

The next round starts with the next player in turn becoming the leader and shooting from a different place. All the same rules apply, except that a player who already has an "H" and misses a shot now gets an "O." (The next time, he would get an "R," and so on). A player who spells "HORSE" is out of the game. The last person left is the winner.

Activity: Fruity Play Dough

Appropriate For: Preschoolers and school-age children

WHAT YOU NEED:

- 1 cup plus 1 tablespoon flour
- 1 package Kool-Aid, any flavor
- ¼ cup salt
- 1 tablespoon vegetable oil
- ⅔ to ¾ cup boiling water
- Medium-sized bowl
- Cookie cutters (optional)

WHAT YOU DO:

Mix the flour, Kool-Aid and salt together in the bowl. Add the oil. Pour the boiling water over the flour mixture in the bowl and mix thoroughly. If the mixture looks too runny, add a little bit more flour, 1 tablespoon at a time, to get the consistency right. Let the mixture cool. When it is cool enough to handle, knead the dough until it is smooth. Now you are ready to play! Let the child mold the play dough into shapes, or make cut-outs using cookie cutters. When you are finished playing, the play dough can be stored in an airtight container in the refrigerator.

NOTES:

- Use extreme caution when boiling the water and pouring it into the bowl.
- Don't let the child eat the play dough!

Activity: Funky Monkey and Very Berry Smoothies

Appropriate For: Toddlers, preschoolers and school-age children

WHAT YOU NEED:

- Blender

For Funky Monkey Smoothies:

- ½ cup ice
- ½ cup milk
- 1 banana, cut in big pieces
- 2 tablespoons peanut butter
- 2 tablespoons chocolate syrup

For Very Berry Smoothies:

- ½ cup frozen blueberries
- ½ cup frozen strawberries
- ½ cup orange juice
- ½ tablespoon honey (optional)
- ½ teaspoon vanilla (optional)

WHAT YOU DO:

Place the smoothie ingredients in the blender and blend until smooth. Pour into glasses or cups. Each recipe makes 2 servings.

NOTES:

- Check with the parents before making and serving these recipes. Some children may have food allergies or other dietary restrictions.

Activity: Paper Bowl Jellyfish

Appropriate For: Preschoolers and school-age children

WHAT YOU NEED:

- Plain white paper bowls
- Watercolor paint and brushes
- Brightly colored ribbon in assorted colors, cut in lengths about 8" to 12" long (ric rac and transparent ribbon are fun to try, but any kind of ribbon will work)
- Glue
- Paste-on eyes from the craft store, or white construction paper, scissors and a black marker (to make eyes)
- Transparent thread (or any kind of thread that you have)
- Needle

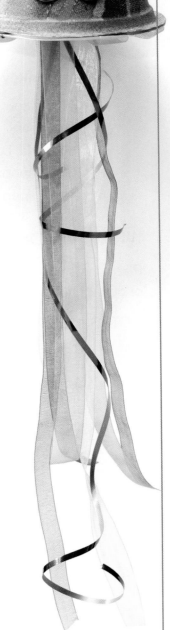

WHAT YOU DO:

Give the child a bowl. Have her turn the bowl over and paint the outside of it with watercolors. After the paint dries, flip the bowl right-side-up. Apply a lot of glue to the inside bottom of the bowl, and lay the ends of pieces of ribbon in the glue. Let the other ends of the ribbons drape over the edge of the bowl. While the glue is still wet, place another paper bowl inside the first, so that the ends of the ribbons are sandwiched in between. Put a can or something heavy in the bowls to weigh them down while the glue dries. After the glue dries, have the child flip the bowl back over, and glue or draw on the eyes. Now, thread the needle with a piece of thread about 12" long. With the jellyfish right-side-up, poke a hole through the center of the bowl, coming up from the bottom and bringing the thread through the hole to the top of the jellyfish. Now put the other end of the thread through the needle and poke a second hole next to the first, coming up from the bottom and bringing the other end of the thread through to the top of the jellyfish. Tie the two ends of the thread together at the top of the jellyfish to form a loose loop. Now, pull the loop down so most of it is underneath the jellyfish. One at a time, pull each piece of ribbon through the loop, so that the jellyfish's "tentacles" are gathered in the middle. When all the pieces of ribbon are gathered in the middle, pull up on the loop from the top to gather the ribbons close to the bottom of the bowl. Now your jellyfish is ready to hang up!

NOTES:

You should use the needle to poke the holes in the jellyfish for the child. Be sure to put the needle and thread away in a safe place when you are finished using them.

Activity: Peanut Butter and Banana Sandwich

Appropriate For: Preschoolers and school-age children

WHAT YOU NEED:

- 2 slices whole-wheat bread
- ¼ banana, sliced
- 2 tablespoons peanut butter
- 2 tablespoons whole-grain flake cereal (optional)

WHAT YOU DO:

Spread the peanut butter on both slices of bread. On one slice of bread, place the banana slices on top of the peanut butter. If you are using the cereal, sprinkle this on top of the peanut butter on the other slice of bread. Sandwich the two slices of bread together. Cut the sandwich into triangles or rectangles and serve. Makes 1 serving.

NOTES:

- Check with the parents before making and serving this recipe. Some children may have food allergies or other dietary restrictions.

Activity: Roll the Ball

Appropriate For: Toddlers

WHAT YOU NEED:

- Soft, round ball

WHAT YOU DO:

Sit on the floor with the child. Say "Catch the ball!" and roll the ball within the child's reach. Then have the child roll the ball back to you.
Once the child gets the hang of this, you can roll the ball beyond the child's reach. You can then encourage the child to "get the ball" and roll it back to you.

Activity: Red Light, Green Light

Appropriate For: Preschoolers and school-age children

WHAT YOU NEED:

- Space to move around freely

WHAT YOU DO:

One child is designated as "It" and stands on an imaginary line, which is the finish line. The rest of the players stand in a straight line about three body lengths away. The commands are "red light" and "green light." The child who is "It" turns his or her back to the players and yells "green light!" On this command, all the players hurry toward the finish line. The child who is "It" then yells "red light!" and spins around to face the other players. On this command, they must all freeze. Anyone the child who is "It" catches moving must return to the starting line. Continue the cycle of having the child who is "It" give "green light" and "red light" commands. The first player to cross the finish line wins and becomes "It" for the next game.

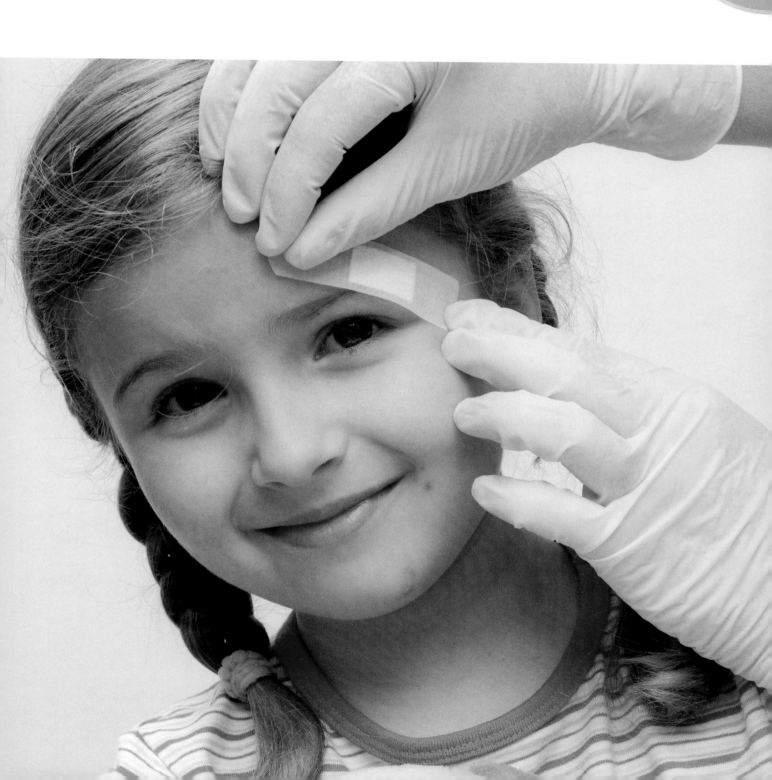

Allergic Reaction, Minor

What to look for:

- A skin rash

- A stuffy nose

- Red, watery eyes

- Exposure to a known trigger (for example: a certain food, a bee sting, animal dander)

What to do:

- Check the child carefully for signals of a more severe allergic reaction. See **ALLERGIC REACTION, SEVERE (ANAPHYLAXIS)**.

Call 9-1-1 or the local emergency number if:

- The child has had a severe allergic reaction before or starts to show signals of a severe allergic reaction. See **ALLERGIC REACTION, SEVERE (ANAPHYLAXIS)**.

Allergic Reaction, Severe (Anaphylaxis)

What to look for:

- Trouble breathing (including coughing or wheezing)

- A feeling of tightness in the chest and throat

- Swelling of the face, neck or tongue

- A rash or hives (large red itchy bumps) that cover the entire body

- Upset stomach (pain, vomiting or diarrhea)

- Dizziness or loss of consciousness

- Shock. See **SHOCK**.

- Exposure to a known trigger (for example: a certain food, a bee sting)

- Medical alert bracelet or necklace

What to do:

- Call 9-1-1 or the local emergency number.

- Encourage the child to use his or her auto-injector and help if necessary.

Call 9-1-1 or the local emergency number if:

- The child is showing signals of a severe allergic reaction.

Animal Bite

What to look for:

- Bite mark (ripped skin or puncture wounds)
- Bleeding
- Pain

What to do:

- Try to get the child away from the animal without putting yourself in danger.

If the wound appears to be minor and was caused by an animal that the child knows:

- Apply direct pressure with a gauze pad to stop the bleeding.
- Wash the area with soap and warm water.
- Dry the area, apply antibiotic ointment if the parents told you it was OK to use, and cover with an adhesive bandage.
- Tell the parents what happened.

If the wound appears severe or was caused by a wild or stray animal:

- Call 9-1-1 or the local emergency number.
- Control the bleeding. See **BLEEDING, SEVERE**.
- Check the child carefully for signals of shock. See **SHOCK**.

Call 9-1-1 or the local emergency number if:

- The wound is severe or bleeding heavily.
- The wound was caused by a wild or stray animal.

Asthma Attack

What to look for:

- Wheezing or coughing

- Rapid, shallow breathing (or trouble breathing)

- Sweating

- Being unable to talk without stopping for a breath

- Tightness in the chest

- Feeling of not being able to get enough air into the lungs

- Feelings of fear or anxiety

- Exposure to a known trigger (for example: cold air, dust, exercise)

- Medical alert bracelet or necklace

What to do:

- Have the child sit down in a comfortable position and lean forward slightly to make breathing easier.

- Encourage the child to use his or her rescue inhaler, and help if necessary.

- Call 9-1-1 or the local emergency number.

Call 9-1-1 or the local emergency number if:

- The child's breathing doesn't improve, or if the child loses consciousness.

Bee Sting

What to look for:

- Stinger

- Pain at the site

- Swelling

- Possible allergic reaction

What to do:

- Use a plastic card to scrape the stinger away from the skin.

- Wash the area with soap and warm water.

- Dry the area, apply antibiotic ointment if the parents told you it was OK to use, and cover with an adhesive bandage.

- Tell the parents what happened.

Call 9-1-1 or the local emergency number if:

- The child is showing signals of a severe allergic reaction, such as trouble breathing. See **ALLERGIC REACTION, SEVERE (ANAPHYLAXIS)**.

Bleeding, Minor

What to look for:

- Minor cut or scrape

- Mild to moderate bleeding

What to do:

- Apply direct pressure with a gauze pad to stop the bleeding.

- Wash the area with soap and warm water.

- Dry the area, apply antibiotic ointment if the parents told you it was OK to use, and cover with an adhesive bandage.

- Tell the parents what happened.

Call 9-1-1 or the local emergency number if:

- The bleeding does not stop after 15 minutes.

- The child shows signals of shock. See **SHOCK**.

Bleeding, Severe

What to look for:

- Deep or large cuts

- Skin or body parts that have been partially or completely torn away

- Heavy bleeding

What to do:

- Call 9-1-1 or the local emergency number.

- Apply direct pressure with a gauze pad. If blood soaks through the first gauze pad, apply additional gauze pads on top.

- Wrap roll gauze around the wound to make a bandage. Tie or tape the bandage to secure it.
- Check the skin on the side of the injury farthest away from the heart—the skin should be warm and its normal color, with normal feeling.
- Continue to apply direct pressure until help arrives.
- Care for shock if necessary. See **SHOCK**.

Call 9-1-1 or the local emergency number if:

- The bleeding does not stop after 15 minutes.
- The child shows signals of shock. See **SHOCK**.

Blister

What to look for:

- Red, tender or sore area on the feet or hands
- Raised "bubble"-like area filled with clear fluid or blood

What to do:

If the blister is not broken:

- Do not puncture or cut the blister.
- Loosely tape a gauze pad over the blister.
- Have the child wear a different pair of shoes if the blister is on a foot.
- Tell the parents what happened.

If the blister is broken:

- Wash the area with soap and warm water.
- Dry the area, apply antibiotic ointment if the parents told you it was OK to use, and cover with an adhesive bandage.
- Tell the parents what happened.

Blood Sugar (Diabetic) Emergency

What to look for:

- Looking or feeling ill

- Dizziness or shakiness

- Headache

- Cool, clammy skin

- Changes in behavior (for example, crankiness)

- Seizures or loss of consciousness

- Medical alert bracelet or necklace

What to do:

- If the child can safely swallow, give sugar, such as:
  - Glucose tablets or gel tube (follow package instructions)
  - 2 tablespoons of raisins
  - 4 ounces (½ cup) of juice or regular soda (nondiet)
  - 1 tablespoon sugar, honey or corn syrup
  - 8 ounces of nonfat or 1 percent milk
  - Hard candies, jellybeans or gumdrops
- Have the child check her blood sugar level, if she knows how.
- Tell the parents what happened.

Call 9-1-1 or the local emergency number if:

- The child does not feel better in about 5 minutes.

- The child loses consciousness or has a seizure.

Bone, Broken

What to look for:

- Pain

- Swelling

- Bruising

- Child is unable or unwilling to move or use the injured body part

- A body part that looks bent, crooked or deformed, or the ends of a broken bone poking through the skin

- A popping, snapping or grating noise at the time of injury

What to do:

- Call 9-1-1 or the local emergency number.

- If the broken bone is poking through the skin, place sterile dressings around the bone as you would for an object that is stuck in the body. See **OBJECT STUCK IN BODY (EMBEDDED OBJECT)**.

- Avoid moving the injured part.

- Otherwise, give general care for a muscle, bone or joint injury. See **MUSCLE, BONE OR JOINT INJURY**.

- Care for shock if necessary. See **SHOCK**.

Call 9-1-1 or the local emergency number if:

- The ends of a broken bone are poking through the skin.

- The injured body part is bent, crooked or looks deformed.

- There is moderate or severe swelling and bruising.

- The child heard or felt a "popping," "snapping" or "grating" sound at the time of the injury.

- The child cannot move or use the injured body part.

- The injured area is cold and numb.

- The injury involves the head, neck or spine.

- The child is having trouble breathing.

- The cause of the injury (for example, a fall from a tree or getting hit by a car) makes you think that the injury may be severe or that the child may have multiple injuries.

- It is not possible to safely or comfortably move the child to a vehicle for transport to a hospital.

Bruise

What to look for:

- Red or purple discoloration of the skin

- Swelling

- Pain

What to do:

- Apply an ice pack or a cold pack wrapped in a towel to the bruise for up to 20 minutes. Wait 1 hour before applying ice or cold again.

- Prop the injured part up, but only if doing so does not cause more pain.

- Discuss any care provided with the parents.

Burn, Chemical

What to look for:

- Chemical on the skin

- Redness or other unusual skin color

- Pain, burning or stinging

What to do:

- Call 9-1-1 or the local emergency number.

- Remove the chemical from the skin.

  - ***If the chemical is dry:*** Put on gloves. Remove clothing that is contaminated by the chemical. Brush the chemical off the skin using a towel, brushing away from the child's body and away from yourself. Rinse the area with a large amount of cool water.

  - ***If the chemical is wet:*** Put on gloves. Remove clothing that is contaminated by the chemical. Rinse the area with a large amount of cool water for at least 20 minutes or until help arrives, rinsing away from the child's body and away from yourself.

Call 9-1-1 or the local emergency number if:

- The burn was caused by chemicals.

Burn, Electrical

What to look for:

- Nearby power source

- Burn marks on the skin (entry and exit of current)

- Loss of consciousness

- Dazed, confused behavior

- Trouble breathing

- Weak or irregular heartbeat, or no heartbeat

What to do:

- Call 9-1-1 or the local emergency number.

- Turn the power off at its source (such as the main circuit breaker). Do not go near downed power lines; if the scene is unsafe, wait for help to arrive.

- Be prepared to give CPR. See **CARDIAC EMERGENCY, CHILD (OLDER THAN 1 YEAR)** or **CARDIAC EMERGENCY, INFANT**.

- Care for shock if necessary. See **SHOCK**.

- Care for the burns. See **BURN, HEAT (THERMAL)**.

Call 9-1-1 or the local emergency number if:

- The burn was caused by electricity.

Burn, Heat (Thermal)

What to look for:

- Red, brown, black or white skin

- Pain (or no pain, if the burn is deep)

- Swelling

- Blisters

What to do:

- Remove the source of the heat. If the child's clothes are on fire, have the child "stop, drop and roll" to put out the flames.

- Cool the burn by rinsing it with large amounts of cool running water.

- Cover the burn loosely with sterile gauze.

- Care for shock if necessary. See **SHOCK**.

- Tell the parents what happened.

Call 9-1-1 or the local emergency number if:

- The burn involves a child (unless the burn is very mild).

- The burn involves the head, neck, mouth or nose.

- The burn involves the hands, feet or groin (the area between the legs).

- The burn covers more than one part of the body or covers a large percentage of the body.

- The burn was caused by chemicals, electricity or an explosion.

Burn, Sun

What to look for:

- Red skin

- Pain

- Swelling

- Blisters

What to do:

- Reassure the child.

- Protect the skin from additional damage by moving out of the sun or applying sunscreen.

- Care for the burn. See **BURN, HEAT (THERMAL)**.

- Care for blisters, if necessary. See **BLISTER**.

- Tell the parents what happened.

Call 9-1-1 or the local emergency number if:

- The burn involves a child (unless the burn is very mild).

- The burn involves the head, neck, mouth or nose.

- The burn involves the hands, feet or groin (the area between the legs).

- The burn covers more than one part of the body or covers a large percentage of the body.

Cardiac Emergency, Child (Older Than 1 Year)

What to look for:

- Sudden collapse

- Loss of consciousness

- No breathing or abnormal breathing

- Rescue breaths make the chest rise.

What to do:

- Have someone call 9-1-1 or the local emergency number. If you are alone, call 9-1-1 or the local emergency number first.

Give CPR:

- Make sure the child is lying face-up, on a firm, flat surface. Kneel beside the child.

- **Give 30 chest compressions.** Place the heel of one hand in the center of the child's chest, with your other hand on top. If you can feel the notch at the end of the child's breastbone, move your hands up a little bit, toward her head. Lean forward so that your shoulders are directly over your hands. This will let you push on the chest using a straight up-and-down motion, which lets you move the most blood with each push and is also less tiring. Keeping your arms straight, push down about 2 inches and then let the chest return to its normal position. Don't take your hands off the child's chest—just your weight. Push hard and push fast! Push at a rate of 100 compressions per minute.

- **Give 2 rescue breaths.** Place the breathing barrier over the child's nose and mouth. Make sure the child's airway is open by keeping the head tilted back. Pinch the nose shut and make a complete seal over the child's mouth with your mouth. Take a normal breath and breathe into the child's mouth for about 1 second. Pause, release the seal, let the air out, then give a second rescue breath. Remember, if the first rescue breath doesn't make the chest clearly rise, retilt the head before giving the second rescue breath. After you have given two rescue breaths, remove the breathing barrier and start another set of 30 chest compressions.

- Once you begin CPR, don't stop. Continue giving sets of 30 chest compressions and 2 rescue breaths until:

  ○ You notice an obvious sign of life, such as breathing.

  ○ An AED is available and ready to use.

  ○ Another trained rescuer (such as an emergency responder) takes over.

  ○ You are too tired to continue.

  ○ The scene becomes unsafe.

Use an AED when one becomes available:

- Turn on the AED.

- Remove the child's shirt and make sure the chest is dry.

- Place the pads.

- If both pads can be placed on the child's chest without touching each other, place one pad on the upper right side of the chest and the other on the left side of the chest.

- If the pads may touch, place one pad in the middle of the child's chest and the other pad on the child's back, between the shoulder blades.

- Plug the connector cable into the AED, if necessary.

- Make sure no one, including you, is touching the child. Say, "EVERYONE STAND CLEAR!"

  ○ Let the AED analyze the heart's rhythm. If the AED tells you to, push the button marked "analyze" to start this process.

  ○ Let the AED deliver a shock, if it determines one is needed. If the AED tells you to, push the button marked "shock" to deliver the shock.

- After the AED delivers the shock, or if no shock is advised:

  ○ Give about 2 minutes of CPR (5 cycles of 30 compressions/2 rescue breaths).

  ○ Follow the prompts of the AED.

  ○ Continue giving CPR and following the AED's prompts until you see an obvious sign of life or help arrives.

Call 9-1-1 or the local emergency number if:

- You saw the child suddenly collapse.

- The child is unconscious.

- The child is not breathing, or is breathing abnormally.

Cardiac Emergency, Infant

What to look for:

- Sudden collapse

- Loss of consciousness

- No breathing or abnormal breathing

- Rescue breaths make the chest rise

What to do:

- Have someone call 9-1-1 or the local emergency number. If you are alone, call 9-1-1 or the local emergency number first.

Give CPR:

- Make sure the infant is lying face-up, on a hard, flat surface.

- **Give 30 chest compressions.** Place two or three fingers on the center of the infant's chest, just below the nipple line. If you feel the notch at the end of the infant's breastbone, move your fingers slightly toward his head. Place your other hand on the infant's forehead and keep the head tilted back so that the chin is straight up-and-down. Press down about 1½ inches and then let the chest return to its normal position. Push hard and push fast! Push at a rate of 100 compressions per minute.

- **Give 2 rescue breaths.** Place the breathing barrier over the infant's nose and mouth. Open the airway. (Tilt the head back until the chin is straight up-and-down.) Make a complete seal over the infant's nose and mouth with your mouth. Take a normal breath and breathe into the infant's mouth for about 1 second. Pause, release the seal, let the air out, then give a second rescue breath. After you have given two rescue breaths, remove the breathing barrier and start another set of 30 chest compressions.

- Once you begin CPR, don't stop. Continue giving sets of 30 chest compressions and 2 rescue breaths until:

    o You notice an obvious sign of life.

    o An AED is ready to use.

    o Another trained rescuer takes over.

    o You are too tired to continue.

    o The scene becomes unsafe.

Use an AED when one becomes available:

- Turn on the AED.

- Remove the infant's shirt and make sure the chest is dry.

- Place one pad in the middle of the infant's chest and the other pad on the infant's back, between the shoulder blades.

- Plug the connector cable into the AED, if necessary.

- Make sure no one, including you, is touching the child. Say, "EVERYONE STAND CLEAR!"

    o Let the AED analyze the heart's rhythm. If the AED tells you to, push the button marked "analyze" to start this process.

    o Let the AED deliver a shock, if it determines one is needed. If the AED tells you to, push the button marked "shock" to deliver the shock.

- After the AED delivers the shock, or if no shock is advised:

    o Give about 2 minutes of CPR (5 cycles of 30 compressions/2 rescue breaths).

    o Follow the prompts of the AED.

    o Continue giving CPR and following the AED's prompts until you see an obvious sign of life or help arrives.

Call 9-1-1 or the local emergency number if:

- You saw the infant suddenly collapse.

- The infant is unconscious.

- The infant is not breathing or is breathing abnormally.

Choking, Conscious Child (Older Than 1 Year)

What to look for:

- Clutching the throat with one or both hands

- A surprised, confused or panicked look on the child's face

- Coughing, either forcefully or weakly, or being totally unable to cough

- Being unable to cry or speak

- High-pitched squeaking noises as the child tries to breathe

- Bluish skin color

- Loss of consciousness (if the choking isn't relieved)

What to do:

If the child can speak or cry and is coughing forcefully:

- Encourage the child to keep coughing.

- If the child is not able to cough up the object quickly, have someone call 9-1-1 or the local emergency number and be ready to give first aid for a conscious choking child.

- Tell the parents what happened.

If the child cannot speak or cry and is coughing weakly or making a high-pitched squeaking noise:

- Have someone call 9-1-1 or the local emergency number immediately.

- Give first aid for a conscious choking child.

- Tell the parents what happened.

If the child cannot speak, cry, cough or breathe (conscious choking child):

- Have someone call 9-1-1 or the local emergency number immediately.

- **Give 5 back blows.** Stand or kneel behind the child. Place one arm diagonally across the child's chest (to provide support). Lean the child forward at the waist so that her upper body is parallel to the ground, and firmly strike the child between the shoulder blades with the heel of your hand.

- **Give 5 abdominal thrusts.** Stand or kneel behind the child. Wrap your arms around the child's waist. Using one or two fingers, find the child's belly button. Make a fist with your other hand and place the thumb side just above the child's belly button. Cover your fist with your other hand and give quick, upward thrusts into the child's abdomen.

- Continue giving sets of 5 back blows and 5 abdominal thrusts until:

  - The object pops out of the child's mouth.

  - The child can cough forcefully, speak or breathe.

  - The child becomes unconscious.

- Tell the parents what happened.

If the child loses consciousness:

- Make sure 9-1-1 or the local emergency number has been called.

- Lower the child to the floor.

- Give first aid for an unconscious choking child older than 1 year, starting with 30 chest compressions. See **CHOKING, UNCONSCIOUS CHILD (Older Than 1 Year)**.

Call 9-1-1 or the local emergency number if:

- The child cannot speak or cry and is coughing weakly or making a high-pitched squeaking noise.

- The child is unable to cry, speak, cough or breathe.

- The child becomes unconscious.

Choking, Conscious Infant

What to look for:

- Coughing, either forcefully or weakly, or being totally unable to cough

- Being unable to cry

- High-pitched squeaking noises as the infant tries to breathe

- Bluish skin color

- Loss of consciousness (if the choking isn't relieved)

What to do:

If the infant can cry and is coughing forcefully:

- Encourage the infant to keep coughing.

- If the infant is not able to cough up the object quickly, have someone call 9-1-1 or the local emergency number and be ready to give first aid for a conscious choking infant.

- Tell the parents what happened.

If the infant cannot cry and is coughing weakly or making a high-pitched squeaking noise:

- Have someone call 9-1-1 or the local emergency number.

- Give first aid for a conscious choking infant.

- Tell the parents what happened.

If the infant cannot cry, cough or breathe (conscious choking infant):

- Have someone call 9-1-1 or the local emergency number.

- Stand, kneel or sit to give first aid to a conscious choking infant. You need to be able to support the infant on your thigh with her head lower than her chest. If the infant is large, you may find it easiest to sit.

- **Give 5 back blows.** Place your forearm along the infant's back, cradling the back of the head with your hand. Place your other forearm along the infant's front, holding the jaw with your thumb and fingers. Turn the infant over so that she is face-down along your forearm. Lower your arm onto your thigh so that the infant's head is lower than her chest.

- Continue to hold the infant's jaw with the thumb and fingers of one hand while you firmly strike the infant between the shoulder blades with the heel of your other hand. Keep your fingers up so that you don't hit the infant's head or neck. Each back blow should be separate from the others.

- **Give 5 chest thrusts.** Place one hand along the infant's back, cradling the back of her head with your hand. While continuing to hold the infant's jaw, support the infant between your forearms and turn her over so that she is face-up along your forearm.

- Lower your arm onto your thigh so that the infant's head is lower than her chest.

- Place the pads of two or three fingers in the center of the infant's chest, on the breastbone. (To find the breastbone, imagine a line across the infant's chest that connects the nipples. Put your fingers just below this imaginary line, in the center of the chest.)

- Press down about 1½ inches and then let the chest return to its normal position.

- Continue giving sets of 5 back blows and 5 chest thrusts until:
  - The object pops out of the infant's mouth.
  - The infant can cough forcefully, cry or breathe.
  - The infant loses consciousness.

- Tell the parents what happened.

If the infant loses consciousness:

- Make sure 9-1-1 or the local emergency number has been called.

- Place the infant on a hard, flat surface.

- Give first aid for an unconscious choking child younger than 1 year, starting with 30 chest compressions. See **CHOKING, UNCONSCIOUS INFANT**.

Call 9-1-1 or the local emergency number if:

- The infant cannot cry and is coughing weakly or making a high-pitched squeaking noise.

- The infant is unable to cry, cough or breathe.

- The infant loses consciousness.

Choking, Unconscious Child (Older Than 1 Year)

What to look for:

- Loss of consciousness

- Rescue breaths do not make the chest rise

- Bluish skin color

What to do:

- Have someone call 9-1-1 or the local emergency number. If you are alone, give 2 minutes of care before calling 9-1-1 or the local emergency number.

- Make sure the child is on his back, on a firm, flat surface. Kneel beside the child.

- **Give 30 chest compressions.** Place the heel of one hand in the center of the child's chest, with your other hand on top. Lean forward so that your shoulders are directly over your hands. Keeping your arms straight, push down about 2 inches, and then let the chest return to its normal position. Push at a rate of 100 compressions per minute.

- **Look for the object.** Grasp the child's lower jaw between your thumb and forefinger and open the mouth. Look for the object. If you see the object, remove it with your finger. If the child is small, use your pinky finger.

Note: *Never put your finger in the child's mouth unless you can actually see the object. If you can't see the object and you put your finger in the child's mouth, you might accidently push the object deeper into the child's throat.*

- **Attempt 2 rescue breaths.** Place the breathing barrier over the child's nose and mouth. Open the airway. (Put one hand on the forehead and two fingers on the bony part of the chin and tilt the head back until the chin is slightly further back than straight up and down.) Pinch the nose shut and make a complete seal over the child's mouth with your mouth. Take a normal breath and breathe into the child's mouth for about 1 second. Release the seal, let the air out, then try to give a second rescue breath.

  - If the breaths make the chest clearly rise, remove the breathing barrier and check for breathing for no more than 10 seconds. Then give care according to the conditions that you find.

  - If the breaths do not go in, repeat the process of giving 30 compressions, looking for the object and giving 2 rescue breaths until the chest clearly rises or the child can cough, speak, cry or breathe on his own.

- Tell the parents what happened.

Call 9-1-1 or the local emergency number if:

- The child loses consciousness.

- The rescue breaths do not make the chest rise.

Choking, Unconscious Infant

What to look for:

- Loss of consciousness

- Rescue breaths do not make the chest rise

- Bluish skin color

What to do:

- Have someone call 9-1-1 or the local emergency number. If you are alone, give 2 minutes of care before calling 9-1-1 or the local emergency number.

- Make sure the infant is on her back, on a firm, flat surface.

- **Give 30 chest compressions.** Place two or three fingers on the center of the infant's chest, just below the nipple line. Place your other hand on the infant's forehead and keep the head tilted back so that the chin is straight up-and-down. Keeping your fingers pointed down, push down about 1½ inches and then let the chest return to its normal position. Push hard and push fast! Aim for a rate of 100 compressions per minute.

- **Look for the object.** Grasp the infant's lower jaw between your thumb and forefinger and open the mouth. Look for the object. If you see the object, remove it with your pinky finger.

Note: Never put your finger in the infant's mouth unless you can actually see the object. If you can't see the object and you put your finger in the infant's mouth, you might accidentally push the object deeper into the infant's throat.

- **Attempt 2 rescue breaths.** Place the breathing barrier over the infant's nose and mouth. Open the airway. (Put one hand on the forehead and two fingers on the bony part of the chin and tilt the head back until the chin is straight up-and-down.) Make a complete seal over the infant's nose and mouth with your mouth. Take a normal breath and breathe into the infant's mouth for about 1 second. Release the seal, let the air out, then try to give a second rescue breath.

  - If the breaths make the chest clearly rise, remove the breathing barrier and check for breathing for no more than 10 seconds. Then give care according to the conditions that you find.

  - If the breaths do not go in, repeat the process of giving 30 compressions, looking for the object and giving 2 rescue breaths until the chest clearly rises or the infant can cough, cry or breathe on her own.

- Tell the parents what happened.

Call 9-1-1 or the local emergency number if:

- The infant loses consciousness.

- The rescue breaths do not make the chest rise.

Cold-Related Illness

See **FROSTBITE** and **HYPOTHERMIA**.

CPR

See **CARDIAC EMERGENCY, CHILD (OLDER THAN 1 YEAR)** and **CARDIAC EMERGENCY, INFANT**.

Diabetic Emergency

See **BLOOD SUGAR (DIABETIC) EMERGENCY**.

Fainting

What to look for:

- Dizziness or weakness

- Sweating

- Pale skin

- Brief loss of consciousness (only 1 to 2 minutes)

What to do:

If the child is about to faint:

- Have the child sit with her head between her knees.

- Tell the parents what happened.

If the child faints:

- Lower the child to the ground and position her on her back.

- Loosen any tight clothing.

- Check to make sure the child is breathing.

- If the child vomits, roll her onto her side.

- Once the child recovers, check her from toe to head for any injuries that might have happened as a result of the fall, and give care according to the conditions that you find and your level of training.

- Tell the parents what happened.

Fever

What to look for:

- Warm or hot skin

- Other signals of illness, such as a headache, muscle aches, chills, loss of appetite or low energy

- Fussiness or quiet and not as active as usual

- Body temperature of 100.4° F (38° C) or higher (when temperature is taken at the mouth, ear or forehead)

- Body temperature of 99° F (37.2° C) or higher (when temperature is taken at the armpit)

- Seizures

What to do:

- Call the parents for additional instructions.

- Take the child's temperature, if you have the parents' permission to do so. Use the thermometer and the method of taking the temperature that the parents tell you to use.

- Reassure the child. Try to keep the child comfortable. Encourage him to rest.

- Give care for seizure, if necessary. See **SEIZURE.**

Call 9-1-1 or the local emergency number if:

- The child loses consciousness.

- The child is having trouble breathing.

- The child has a seizure that lasts longer than 5 minutes, or several seizures in a row.

Frostbite

What to look for:

- Cold, "waxy" skin that may be white, yellow, blue, red or (in severe cases) black

- Numbness or loss of feeling in the area

- Blisters (in severe cases)

What to do:

- Get the child to a warmer place.

- Don't try to rewarm the area if there is a chance it could freeze again.

- Handle the frostbitten area gently. Never rub it.

If the frostbite is minor (no blackened areas or blisters):

- Gradually rewarm the frostbitten part by cupping it in your warm hands.

- When the frostbitten area has thawed out, loosely bandage the area with dry sterile gauze. If fingers or toes are frostbitten, place dry sterile gauze between them to keep them separated.

- Tell the parents what happened so that they can follow up with the child's doctor.

In cases of mild frostbite:

- If medical help is not readily available and you are sure that the area will not freeze again, rewarm the frostbitten area by soaking it in warm water (100° F–105° F) until normal color returns and the frostbitten area feels warm. Then loosely bandage the frostbitten area with dry sterile gauze.

If the frostbite is severe (blackened skin or blisters):

- Call 9-1-1 or the local emergency number.

- Take actions to prevent hypothermia. See **HYPOTHERMIA**.

- *Do not* try to rewarm an area with severe frostbite.

Call 9-1-1 or the local emergency number if:

- The frostbite is severe (the skin has turned black or is blistered).

Head, Neck, or Spinal Injury

What to look for:

- The child was hit by a car, thrown from a moving car, or was in a car accident and was not properly secured in a child safety seat.

- The child is wearing a safety helmet that is broken.

- The child was injured as a result of a fall from a height greater than his own height.

- The child says he has neck or back pain.

- The child says his arms or legs feel "tingly."

©2014 American Red Cross | Advanced Child Care Training

- The child is not fully alert.

- The child is unable to move or staggers when trying to walk.

- The child appears to be weak.

What to do:

- Call 9-1-1 or the local emergency number.

If the child is conscious:

- Place your hands on both sides of the child's head, keeping it in the position you found it. If the head is sharply turned to the side, do not move it.

If the child is unconscious:

- Follow the steps for checking an unconscious child. Carefully tilt the head and lift the chin just enough to open the airway. See **UNCONSCIOUS CHILD, CHECKING**.

Call 9-1-1 or the local emergency number if:

- You think the child might have a head, neck or spinal injury.

Heat-Related Illness

What to look for:

Heat cramps

- Painful muscle spasms, usually in the legs and stomach

Heat exhaustion

- Pale/gray or red skin that is cool and moist

- Heavy sweating

- Headache

- Dizziness

- Upset stomach (nausea or vomiting)

Heat stroke

- Hot, red skin that may be moist or dry

- Confusion

- Loss of consciousness

- Rapid, shallow breathing

- Rapid, weak heartbeat

- Vomiting

What to do:

- Move the child to a cooler place.

Heat cramps

- Give small sips of a sports drink, milk, juice or water.

- Lightly stretch the muscle and rub the area to relieve the cramps.

- Watch for signals of heat exhaustion or heat stroke.

- Tell the parents what happened.

Heat exhaustion

- Loosen or remove as much clothing as possible.

- Apply cool, wet cloths to the skin or mist the child with cool water. Fanning the child may also help.

- If the child is conscious, give small sips of a sports drink, milk, juice or water.

- Tell the parents what happened.

Heat stroke

- Call 9-1-1 or the local emergency number.

- Rapidly cool the body by removing as much clothing as possible. Apply cool, wet cloths to the skin or mist the child with cool water. Keep the air moving around the child (for example, by fanning the child).

- Prepare to give CPR if the child becomes unconscious. See **CARDIAC EMERGENCY, CHILD (OLDER THAN 1 YEAR)** and **CARDIAC EMERGENCY, INFANT**.

Call 9-1-1 or the local emergency number if:

- The child's condition does not improve quickly.

- The child refuses to drink.

- The child vomits.

- The child loses consciousness.

- The child has signals of heat stroke.

Hypothermia

What to look for:

- Shivering (but may be absent if hypothermia is severe)

- "Glassy" stare

- Numbness

- Indifferent attitude (seeming not to care about anything)

- Loss of consciousness

What to do:

- Get the child to a warmer place.

- Remove any wet clothing and dry the child.

- Help the child to warm up gradually by dressing her in dry clothing (including a hat, gloves and socks) and wrapping her in a blanket.

- If the child is alert, give her small sips of a warm liquid.

- Don't try to rewarm the child too quickly (for example, by putting her in a hot bath or shower). Rapid rewarming can lead to dangerous heart rhythms.

Call 9-1-1 or the local emergency number if:

- The child is unconscious.

- The child does not seem to be responding to first aid.

Muscle, Bone, or Joint Injury

What to look for:

- Pain

- Swelling

- Bruising

- The child is unable or unwilling to move or use the injured body part

- A body part that looks bent, crooked or deformed or a broken bone poking through the skin

- A popping, snapping or grating noise at the time of injury

What to do:

RICE

- **R** stands for rest. Don't allow the child to use the injured body part.

- **I** stands for immobilize. Keep the injured body part in the position it was found.

- **C** stands for cold. Apply a cold pack or an ice pack wrapped in a dry towel to the area to reduce swelling and pain. Apply the cold pack or ice pack for no more than 20 minutes at a time, and wait at least 1 hour before applying the cold or ice pack again.

- **E** stands for elevate. Prop the injured part up, but only if doing so does not cause more pain.

Splinting

- Splinting should only be used when the victim needs to be transported.

- Choose a material to make the splint.

- Check the skin on the side of the injury farthest away from the heart for feeling, warmth and color.

- Make the splint:

  ○ **Soft splint:** Fold several triangular bandages into ties and place them under the injured body part, above and below the area. Wrap the soft object you are using as a splint (for example: a towel, blanket or pillow) around the injured area. Tie the triangular bandages around the splint to secure it.

  ○ **Rigid splint:** Fold several triangular bandages into ties. Place the splint under the injured body part. Tie the triangular bandages around the splint to secure it.

  ○ **Anatomic (body part) splint:** Fold several triangular bandages into ties. Place the uninjured body part next to the injured body part. Tie the triangular bandages around the two body parts to secure them to each other.

  ○ **Sling:** Place a triangular bandage under the arm so that one point of the triangle is over the uninjured shoulder, one point is near the hand or elbow of the injured arm and one point hangs straight down. Bring the point that is

©2014 American Red Cross | Advanced Child Care Training

hanging straight down up over the injured shoulder and tie the ends of the sling at the side of the neck. Fold a triangular bandage into a tie and use it to bind the injured arm to the chest.

- Recheck for feeling, warmth and color.

Call 9-1-1 or the local emergency number if:

- A broken bone is poking through the skin.

- The injured body part is bent, crooked or looks deformed.

- There is moderate or severe swelling and bruising.

- The child heard or felt a "popping," "snapping" or "grating" sound at the time of the injury.

- The child cannot move or use the injured body part.

- The injured area is cold and numb.

- The injury involves the head, neck or spine.

- The child is having trouble breathing.

- The cause of the injury (for example, a fall from a tree or getting hit by a car) makes you think that the injury may be severe, or that the child may have multiple injuries.

- It is not possible to safely or comfortably move the child to a vehicle for transport to a hospital.

Nosebleed

What to look for:

- Bleeding from one or both nostrils

What to do:

- Reassure the child.

- Have the child sit down and lean slightly forward.

- If the child is old enough, ask him to pinch his nostrils together, or you can do this for the child (remember to put on your disposable gloves first!).

- Check after 5 minutes to see if the bleeding has stopped. If it has not, continue to pinch the nostrils shut for another 5 minutes.

- If after 10 minutes the bleeding has not stopped, hold a cold pack or an ice pack wrapped in a towel against the bridge of the nose while continuing to pinch the nostrils shut.

- Tell the parents what happened.

Call 9-1-1 or the local emergency number if:

- The nosebleed continues for more than 15 to 20 minutes.

- The bleeding is severe or gushing.

Object Stuck in Body (Embedded Object)

What to look for:

- An object in an open wound

- Pain

- Bleeding

What to do:

- Call 9-1-1 or the local emergency number.

- Don't try to remove the object.

- Place several dressings around the object to support the object in place.

- Bandage the dressings in place around the object.

- Notify the parents.

Call 9-1-1 or the local emergency number if:

- There is an object embedded in an open wound.

Poisoning

What to look for:

- Upset stomach (nausea or vomiting) or stomach pain

- Headache

- Dizziness

- Drowsiness

- Loss of consciousness

- Trouble breathing

- Sweating

- Seizures

- Open or spilled container nearby

- Overturned or damaged plant nearby

- Unusual odors

- Burns around the lips or tongue or on the skin

- Residue on the child's lips, face or tongue

- Strange odor on the child's breath

What to do:

- Call the National Poison Control Center (PCC) Hotline at 800-222-1222 and follow the dispatcher's instructions. If the child is unconscious, having trouble breathing or having a seizure, call 9-1-1 or the local emergency number first!

- If possible, tell the dispatcher what the poison was, how much the child swallowed and when the child swallowed it.

- Don't give the child anything to eat or drink unless the dispatcher tells you to.

- If the child vomits, position her on her side in the recovery position.

Call 9-1-1 or the local emergency number if:

- The child is unconscious.

- The child is having trouble breathing.

- The child is having a seizure.

Scorpion Sting

What to look for:

- Bite mark

- Pain, tingling, burning or numbness at the site

- Trouble breathing, seizures or total-body numbness (rare)

What to do:

- Call 9-1-1 or the local emergency number.
- Wash the area with soap and warm water.
- Apply an ice pack or a cold pack wrapped in a towel to the site.

Call 9-1-1 or the local emergency number if:

- You think a child has been stung by a scorpion.
- The child is having trouble breathing or showing other signals of a severe reaction.

Seizure

What to look for:

- Loss of consciousness
- Uncontrollable shaking or jerking

What to do:

- Call 9-1-1 or the local emergency number. If the child is known to have a condition that causes seizures (such as epilepsy), the parents may prefer that you call them instead.
- Move furniture or other objects that could cause injury out of the way.
- When the seizure is over, check the child as you would an unconscious child. See **UNCONSCIOUS CHILD, CHECKING**.
- Make sure the child's airway is open.
- If there is fluid in the child's mouth (such as pooled saliva, blood or vomit), roll the child onto her side to drain fluids from the mouth.
- Comfort and stay with the child until she is fully conscious or the emergency responders arrive.

Call 9-1-1 or the local emergency number if:

- The child has a seizure.

Shock

What to look for:

- Restlessness or crankiness

- Drowsiness, confusion or loss of consciousness

- Pale or gray, cool, moist skin

- Upset stomach (nausea or vomiting)

- Thirst

- Rapid breathing and heartbeat

What to do:

- Call 9-1-1 or the local emergency number.

- If the child is bleeding, control the bleeding.

- Keep the child from becoming chilled or overheated.

- Don't give the child anything to eat or drink.

- Reassure the child. Try to keep the child comfortable.

Call 9-1-1 or the local emergency number if:

- The child shows signals of shock.

Snake Bite

What to look for:

- Bite mark (two puncture wounds)

- Pain

- Swelling

What to do:

- Call 9-1-1 or the local emergency number.

- Wash the area with soap and warm water.

- Check the skin on the side of the injury farthest away from the heart for feeling, warmth and color.

- Bandage the site snugly with roll gauze. Begin wrapping at the side of the injury farthest away from the heart.

- Recheck for feeling, warmth and color.

Call 9-1-1 or the local emergency number if:

- You think a child has been bitten by a snake.

Snake Bite, Venomous

What to look for:

- Bite mark (two puncture wounds)

- Pain

- Swelling

What to do:

- If the bite is from a venomous snake such as a rattlesnake, copperhead, cottonmouth or coral snake, call 9-1-1 or the local emergency number immediately!

- Wash the area with soap and warm water.

- Apply an elastic (pressure immobilization) bandage to slow the spread of venom through the lymphatic system by following these steps:

  o Check for feeling, warmth and color of the limb, and note changes in skin color and temperature.

  o Place the end of the bandage against the skin and use overlapping turns.

  o The wrap should cover a long body section, such as an arm or a calf, beginning at the point farthest from the heart. For a joint, such as the knee or ankle, use figure eight turns to support the joint.

  o Check above and below the injury for feeling, warmth and color, especially fingers and toes, after you have applied an elastic roller bandage. By checking before and after bandaging, you may be able to tell if any tingling or numbness is from the elastic bandage or the injury.

- Check the snugness of the bandaging—a finger should easily, but not loosely, pass under the bandage.

- Keep the injured area still and lower than the heart. The child should walk only if absolutely necessary.

- *Do not* apply ice.

- *Do not* cut the wound.

- *Do not* apply suction

- *Do not* apply a tourniquet.

- *Do not* use electric shock, such as from a car battery.

Call 9-1-1 or the local emergency number if:

- You think a child has been bitten by a venomous snake.

Spider Bite

What to look for:

- Bite mark

- Pain, stinging or itching at the site

- Swelling

What to do:

- Wash the area with soap and warm water.

- Dry the area, apply antibiotic ointment if the parents told you it was OK to use, and cover with an adhesive bandage.

- Tell the parents what happened.

Call 9-1-1 or the local emergency number if:

- You think a child has been bitten by a brown recluse, black widow or northwestern brown (hobo) spider.

Splinter

What to look for:

- A small piece of wood stuck in the skin
- Pain at the site

What to do:

- Use tweezers to remove the splinter. (If the splinter is too deep and you cannot remove it easily, stop and call the parents.)
- Wash the area with soap and warm water.
- Rinse the area under warm running water for about 5 minutes.
- Dry the area, apply antibiotic ointment if the parents told you it was OK to use, and cover with an adhesive bandage.
- Tell the parents what happened.
- If the splinter is in the eye, do not attempt to remove it! Call 9-1-1 or the local emergency number.

Call 9-1-1 or the local emergency number if:

- The splinter is in the eye.

Stroke

What to look for:

- Sudden weakness or numbness of the face, arm or leg, usually on one side
- Facial drop or drooling
- Sudden difficulty speaking or being understood when speaking
- Sudden loss of vision, or sudden blurred or dimmed vision in one or both eyes
- Sudden severe headache
- Dizziness, confusion, agitation or other altered mental status
- Loss of consciousness
- Loss of balance or coordination, trouble walking or ringing in the ears
- Incontinence

What to do:

- Do a **FAST** check:

    - **F**ace. Ask the child to smile. Is there weakness or drooping on one side of the face?

    - **A**rm. Ask the child to raise both arms. Is there weakness or drooping of one of the arms?

    - **S**peech. Ask the child to say a simple sentence or phrase. Does the child have trouble speaking or is her speech slurred?

    - **T**ime. If the child has trouble responding to your requests or is showing any signals of stroke, call 9-1-1 or the local emergency number immediately.

- If the child is unconscious, make sure he has an open airway and care for life-threatening conditions. If fluid or vomit is in the child's mouth, position him on one side to allow fluids to drain out of the mouth. Remove any material from the mouth with a finger if the child is unconscious. Stay with the child, and monitor breathing and for any changes in the child's condition.

- If the child is conscious, check for non-life-threatening conditions. A stroke can make the child fearful and anxious. Often, he does not understand what has happened. Offer comfort and reassurance. Have the child rest in a comfortable position. Do not give him anything to eat or drink.

Call 9-1-1 or the local emergency number if:

- The child shows signals of stroke.

Sunburn

See **BURN, SUN**.

Tick Bite

What to look for:

- A tick on the skin

What to do:

- Using fine-tipped tweezers, grasp the tick at the head as close to the skin as possible. Pull slowly, steadily and firmly without twisting.

- Seal the tick in a container with rubbing alcohol.

- Wash the area with soap and warm water.

- Dry the area, apply antibiotic ointment if the parents told you it was OK to use, and cover with an adhesive bandage.

- Tell the parents what happened.

Tooth, Knocked Out

What to look for:

- Broken or missing tooth

- Bleeding from the mouth

What to do:

- If the child is conscious, rinse out the mouth with cold tap water, if available.

- Have the child bite down on a rolled sterile dressing in the space left by the tooth to stop bleeding.

- Find and save the tooth. Pick the tooth up by the crown (white part), not the root. Place the tooth in milk, if possible, or cool water.

- Call the parents. The child must be taken to the dentist immediately.

Call 9-1-1 or the local emergency number if:

- The child is unconscious.

- You think the child might have a head, neck or back injury.

- The child has multiple injuries.

Unconscious Child, Checking

What to look for:

- The child is lying on the ground

- The child is not speaking, crying or moving

- The child does not respond when you tap her shoulder (or the bottom of her foot, if the child is younger than 1 year) and ask her in a loud voice if she is OK

What to do:

- If the child is face-down, roll her face-up, keeping the head, neck and back straight.

- Open the airway by placing one hand on the forehead and two fingers on the bony part of the chin and tilting the head back.

  - **For a child older than 1 year:** Tilt the head until the chin is slightly farther back than straight up-and-down.

  - **For an infant:** Tilt the head until the chin is straight up-and-down.

- Look, listen and feel for normal breathing for no more than 10 seconds. If the child is not breathing normally, give 2 rescue breaths.

  - **For a child older than 1 year:** Place a breathing barrier, if you have one, over the child's nose and mouth. With the airway open, pinch the nose shut and make a complete seal over the child's mouth with your mouth. Take a normal breath and breathe into the child's mouth for about 1 second. Release the seal, let the air out, then give a second rescue breath.

  - **For an infant:** Place a breathing barrier, if you have one, over the infant's nose and mouth. With the airway open, make a complete seal over the infant's nose and mouth with your mouth. Take a normal breath and breathe into the infant's mouth for about 1 second. Release the seal, let the air out, then give a second rescue breath.

- Quickly scan for severe bleeding.

- Make sure 9-1-1 or the local emergency number has been called and give care according to the conditions that you find.

Call 9-1-1 or the local emergency number if:

- The child is unconscious.

Sources

"2010 American Heart Association and American Red Cross Guidelines for First Aid." 2010. *Circulation* 122 (suppl. 3): S934–S946.

"2010 American Heart Association Guidelines for Cardiopulmonary Resuscitation and Emergency Cardiovascular Care Science." 2010. *Circulation* 122 (18): Supplement.

About.com. "Childcare." http://childcare. about.com.

American Academy of Child and Adolescent Psychiatry. http://www. aacap.org.

American Academy of Pediatric Dentistry. "Frequently Asked Questions." http://www.aapd.org/resources/ frequently_asked_questions/#35.

American Academy of Pediatric Dentistry. http://www.aapd.org.

American Academy of Pediatrics. "Healthy Children." http://www. healthychildren.org.

American Academy of Pediatrics. http:// www.aap.org/.

American Library Association. www.ala.org.

American Red Cross. 2011. *A Family Guide to First Aid and Emergency Preparedness.* Washington, DC: The American National Red Cross.

American Red Cross. 2011. *First Aid/CPR/AED Participants Manual.* Washington, DC: The American National Red Cross.

American Red Cross. 2013. *Nurse Assistant Training.* Washington, DC: The American National Red Cross.

American Red Cross. 2014. *Swimming and Water Safety.* Washington, DC: The American National Red Cross.

AskDrSears.com. http://askdrsears.com.

Burn Foundation. "Safety Facts on Scald Burns." http://www.burnfoundation.org/ programs/resource.cfm?c=1&a=3.

Calgary Police Service. "Kids & Teens." http://www.calgarypolice.ca/kids-babysitting.html.

Castillo, M, "CDC: Warning labels on cough, cold medicines curbed kids' ER visits." http://www.cbsnews.com/news/ cdc-warning-labels-on-cough-cold-medicines-curbed-kids-er-visits/.

Center for Effective Parenting. http:// www.parenting-ed.org.

Centers for Disease Control and Prevention. "Attention-Deficit/ Hyperactivity Disorder (ADHD)." http:// www.cdc.gov/ncbddd/adhd/data.html.

Centers for Disease Control and Prevention. "Facts About Lyme Disease." http://www.cdc.gov/lyme/.

Centers for Disease Control and Prevention. "Handwashing: Clean Hands Save Lives." http://www.cdc.gov/ handwashing/.

Centers for Disease Control and Prevention. "Important Milestones: Your Baby at Nine Months." http://www.cdc.gov/ncbddd/actearly/milestones/milestones-9mo.html.

Centers for Disease Control and Prevention. "Injury Prevention and Control: Home and Recreational Safety." http://www.cdc.gov/homeandrecreationalsafety/water-safety/waterinjuries-factsheet.html.

Centers for Disease Control and Prevention. "Preventing Shaken Baby Syndrome: A Guide for Health Departments and Community-Based Organizations." http://www.cdc.gov/Concussion/pdf/Preventing_SBS_508-a.pdf.

Centers for Disease Control and Prevention. "Sudden Unexpected Infant Death and Sudden Infant Death Syndrome." http://www.cdc.gov/sids/.

Child Trends. http://www.childtrends.org/.

Childcare Aware of North Dakota. "Medication Administration." http://www.ndchildcare.org/providers/health-safety/medication.html.

Childhelp. 2011. "Childhelp National Child Abuse Hotline." Retrieved December 28, http://www.childhelp.org/pages/hotline-home.

Children, Youth and Families Education and Resource Network. www.cyfernet.org.

Clemson Cooperative Extension. "Food Safety for Pregnant Women & Their Babies." http://www.clemson.edu/extension/hgic/food/food_safety/illnesses/hgic3640.html.

Consumer Product Safety Commission. "Infants and Toddlers Can Strangle in Baby Monitor Cords." http://www.cpsc.gov/cpscpub/pubs/5066.pdf.

Consumer Product Safety Commission. "Ingested Magnets Can Cause Serious Intestinal Injuries." http://www.cpsc.gov/PageFiles/128927/5221.pdf.

Department of the U.S. Army. "Hooah4health." http://www.hooah4health.com.

Fire Prevention Canada. "Babysitter's Guide to Fire Safety—Canada." http://www.fiprecan.ca/sheets/babysitter_guide.pdf.

First Candle. http://www.firstcandle.org/.

Florida Poison Information Center. "Hand Sanitizer Gels." http://pediatrics.med.miami.edu/documents/Hand_Sanitizers.pdf.

Food Allergy Research & Education. "Communicating with Babysitters and Other Caregivers." http://www.foodallergy.org/tools-and-resources/managing-food-allergies/babysitters-and-caregivers.

Healthy Children. "Developmental Milestones: 3 to 4 Year Olds." http://www.healthychildren.org/English/ages-stages/toddler/pages/Developmental-Milestones-3-to-4-Years-Old.aspx.

Healthy Children. "How to Please Fussy Eaters." http://www.healthychildren.org/english/healthy-living/nutrition/pages/How-To-Please-Fussy-Eaters.aspx?nfstatus=401&nftoken=00000000-0000-0000-0000-000000000000&nfstatusdescription=ERROR%3a+No+local+token.

Healthy Children. "Make Baby's Room Safe." http://www.healthychildren.org/English/safety-prevention/at-home/pages/Make-Babys-Room-Safe.aspx.

Healthy Children. "Reduce the Risk of SIDS." http://www.healthychildren.org/English/ages-stages/baby/sleep/Pages/Preventing-SIDS.aspx.

Holtzman, D. S. 2009. *The Safe Baby: A Do-It Yourself Guide to Home Safety and Healthy Living.* Boulder, CO: Sentient Publications.

Humans Guide. "Ten Positive Ways to Wake Your Kid Up for School." http://humansguide.com/ten-positive-ways-to-wake-your-kids-up-for-school.

Johnson, D. W., and Johnson, F. P. 2003. *Joining Together: Group Theory and Group Skills.* Boston: Allyn & Bacon.

Johnson, D. W., and Johnson, R. T. 1997. *Learning to Lead Teams: Developing Leadership Skills.* Edina, MN: Interaction Book Company.

Johnson, D. W., Johnson, R. T., and Holubec, E. J. 1998. *Cooperation in the Classroom,* revised edition. Edina, MN: Interaction Book Company.

Kids Eat Right. "Water: Go with the Flow." http://www.eatright.org/kids/article.aspx?id=6442470651.

Kids Health. "Why Healthy Teeth Are Important." http://kidshealth.org/kid/stay_healthy/body/teeth_care.html#.

Kids Health. www.KidsHealth.org.

March of Dimes. "Feeding Your Baby." http://www.marchofdimes.com/baby/feeding_foodsafety.html.

Mayo Clinic. "Infant Formula: Your Questions Answered." http://www.mayoclinic.com/health/infant-formula/PR00058/NSECTIONGROUP=2%20%20%20Mayo%20clinic.

McClure, R. "Top 10 Morning Madness Tips for Getting Kids up and Ready." http://childcare.about.com/od/behaviors/tp/gettingkidsup.htm.

McGruff Safe Kids. "Total Identification System." www.mcgruff-tid.com.

Missouri Families. "What to Do About Biting?" http://missourifamilies.org/FEATURES/parentingarticles/parenting1.htm.

NannyPro.com. "How Nannies and Parents Can Prevent Medication Miscommunication." http://www.nannypro.com/blog/how-nannies-and-parents-can-prevent-medication-miscommunication/.

National Association of Child Care Resource and Referral Agencies. "Community-Based Child Care for Military Families: A Booklet for Civilian Child Care Providers." http://www.infanttoddler.com/wp-content/uploads/2011/06/community-based-child-care-for-military-families.pdf.

National Crime Prevention Council. www.ncpc.org/.

National Fire Protection Association. http://www.nfpa.org.

National Heart, Lung, and Blood Institute. National Institutes of Health. http://www.nhlbi.nih.gov/.

National Highway Traffic Safety Administration. "Parents Central: From Car Seats to Car Keys: Keeping Kids Safe." http://www.safercar.gov/parents/index.htm.

National Highway Traffic Safety Administration. "Tips to Increase Your Child's Pedestrian Safety." http://www.nhtsa.gov/parents/walk/NHS1-33758_Par_walk_koko.pdf.

National Highway Traffic Safety Administration. "What Is Distracted Driving?" http://www.distraction.gov/content/get-the-facts/facts-and-statistics.html.

National Network for Child Care. www.nncc.org/.

Norman, M., and Munson, M. K. 1992. Leadership skills you never outgrow. In *Leadership Project Book II: Individual Skills for Older Members.* Champaign, IL: University of Illinois Cooperative Extension Service.

North Carolina Healthy Start Foundation. "Baby's Care and Development: Your Newborn." http://www.nchealthystart.org/public/babycare/newborn.htm.

PBS. "Webonauts Internet Academy." http://pbskids.org/webonauts/.

Pistiner, M. "Food Allergy: Babysitting and Drop-Off Form." http://allergyhome.wpengine.netdna-cdn.com/wp-content/uploads/2013/07/Food_Allergy_Babysitter_DropOff_Emergency_Form.pdf.

Pool Safely. "Pool and Spa Safety." http://www.poolsafely.gov.

Safe Kids Worldwide. "Babysitter Safety." http://www.safekids.org/safety-basics/safety-spotlight/babysitter-safety/.

Safe Kids Worldwide. "Battery Safety." http://www.safekids.org/safety-basics/safety-spotlight/battery-safety/.

Safe Kids Worldwide. "Burn Awareness Week: February 6-12, 2011." http://www.safekids.org/safety-basics/safety-spotlight/Burn-awareness-week/.

Safe Kids Worldwide. "Finding Suitable Toys for Your Children." http://www.safekids.org/assets/docs/safety-basics/safety-tips-by-risk-area/pocket-guide-to-safe-and-age-appropriate-toys.pdf.

Safe Kids Worldwide. "Heatstroke." http://www.safekids.org/heatstroke.

State of Alaska Health and Social Services. "WIC–Bottle Feeding FAQs." http://www.hss.state.ak.us/dpa/programs/nutri/wic/Participants/WICFAQ-bottlefeeding.htm.

Students Against Destructive Decisions. www.saddonline.com.

U.S. Department of Agriculture. "Babies and Food Safety." http://www.fsis.usda.gov/News_&_Events/script_baby_fs/index.asp.

U.S. Department of Agriculture ChooseMyPlate.gov. "Dairy Group: Get Your Calcium-Rich Foods." http://www.choosemyplate.gov/preschoolers/daily-food-plans/about-dairy.html.

U.S. Department of Agriculture ChooseMyPlate.gov. "MyPlate Kids' Place." http://www.choosemyplate.gov/kids/index.html.

U.S. Department of Defense. http://www.defense.gov/.

U.S. Department of Health and Human Services. "HRSA Maternal and Child Health." http://mchb.hrsa.gov/.

U.S. Department of Homeland Security. www.dhs.gov.

U.S. Environmental Protection Agency. "SunWise Program." http://www.epa.gov/sunwise/.

U.S. Food and Drug Administration. "Daily Medicine Record for Your Child." http://www.fda.gov/Drugs/ResourcesForYou/Consumers/BuyingUsingMedicineSafely/UnderstandingOver-the-CounterMedicines/SafeUseofOver-the-CounterPainRelieversandFeverReducers/ucm233848.htm.

U.S. Food and Drug Administration. "Food Safety for Moms-to-Be." http://www.fda.gov/Food/ResourcesForYou/HealthEducators/ucm089629.htm.

U.S. National Library of Medicine. "Infant—Newborn Development." http://www.nlm.nih.gov/medlineplus/ency/article/002004.htm.

U.S. National Library of Medicine. "Shaken Baby Syndrome." http://www.ncbi.nlm.nih.gov/pubmedhealth/.

U.S. National Library of Medicine. "Temper Tantrums." http://www.nlm.nih.gov/medlineplus/ency/article/001922.htm.

University of Florida. "UF/IFAS Extension Solutions." http://solutionsforyourlife.ufl.edu/.

University of Illinois Extension. "A Guide to the Business of Babysitting." http://urbanext.illinois.edu/babysitting/safety.html.

University of Michigan Health System. "Babysitter Safety—What Parents and Sitters Need to Know." http://www.med.umich.edu/yourchild/topics/babysit.htm.

University of Michigan Health System. "Childproofing and Safety at Home." http://www.med.umich.edu/yourchild/topics/safehome.htm.

University of Michigan Health System. "Choking Prevention." http://www.med.umich.edu/yourchild/topics/choking.htm.

University of Minnesota Center for Early Education and Development. "Tip Sheets." http://cehd.umn.edu/ceed/publications/tipsheets/default.html.

WebMD. "Babies' Sleep Position and Sudden Infant Death Syndrome—Topic Overview." http://www.webmd.com/a-to-z-guides/babies-sleep-position-and-sudden-infant-death-syndrome-topic-overview.

WebMD. "Brushing and Flossing Children's Teeth." http://www.webmd.com/oral-health/guide/brushing-flossing-child-teeth.

WebMD. "Making Sense of OTC Drug Use in Kids." http://children.webmd.com/features/making-sense-otc-drug-use-kids.

WebMD. "The Facts About Bottle Feeding." http://www.webmd.com/parenting/baby/bottle-feeding-9/slideshow-bottle-feeding.

Zero to Three. www.zerotothree.org/.

Photography Credits

120   Image © GouraudStudio, 2014. Used under license from Shutterstock.com

121   © iStockphoto.com/duckycards

125   © iStockphoto.com/NickyBlade

125   Image © alexmillos, 2014. Used under license from Shutterstock.com

CHAPTER 7:
PAGE

136   Image © Lightspring, 2014. Used under license from Shutterstock.com

CHAPTER 8:
PAGE

147   Image © JaimieDuplass, 2014. Used under license from Shutterstock.com

148   Image © Rob Byron, 2014. Used under license from Shutterstock.com

153   Image © AlinuteSilzeviciute, 2014. Used under license from Shutterstock.com

154   Image © maximibragimov, 2014. Used under license from Shutterstock.com

156   Image © MarioCigic, 2014. Used under license from Shutterstock.com

158   © iStockphoto.com/lostinbids

159   Image © sunabesyou, 2014. Used under license from Shutterstock.com

160   © iStockphoto.com/RBFried

161   Image © Nitr, 2014. Used under license from Shutterstock.com

163   Image © HenrikLarson, 2014. Used under license from Shutterstock.com

163   Image © PeterWaters, 2014. Used under license from Shutterstock.com

164   © iStockphoto.com/AlasdairJames

166   © iStockphoto.com/GlobalP

166   © iStockphoto.com/GlobalP

167   © iStockphoto.com/Jackscoldsweat-blood

168   Image © tulpahn, 2014. Used under license from Shutterstock.com

168   © iStockphoto.com/BartCo

169   © iStockphoto.com/ozdigital

171   Image © SCOTTCHAN, 2014. Used under license from Shutterstock.com

171   Image © SCOTTCHAN, 2014. Used under license from Shutterstock.com

171   Image © SCOTTCHAN, 2014. Used under license from Shutterstock.com

171   Image © SCOTTCHAN, 2014. Used under license from Shutterstock.com

172   Image © iPortret, 2014. Used under license from Shutterstock.com

182   © iStockphoto.com/MachineHeadz

182   © iStockphoto.com/elsauria

182   © iStockphoto.com/Arcurs

183   © iStockphoto.com/steele2123

APPENDIX A:
PAGE

190   Image © luminaimages, 2014. Used under license from Shutterstock.com

APPENDIX B:
PAGE

210   Image © Blend Images, 2014. Used under license from Shutterstock.com

APPENDIX A:
PAGE

231   © iStockphoto.com/sept2004

232   Image © urbanlight, 2014. Used under license from Shutterstock.com

233   © iStockphoto.com/HelpingHandPhotos

233   © iStockphoto.com/Blue_Cutler

235   © iStockphoto.com/ktaylorg

237   © iStockphoto.com/Snappy_girl

237   © iStockphoto.com/andipantz

238   © iStockphoto.com/monkeybusinessimages

APPENDIX D:
PAGE

239   Image © gorillaimages, 2014. Used under license from Shutterstock.com

Index

9-1-1
accidental calls to, 126
calling, 124–125

A
ABC fire extinguisher, 49
ABCs (airway, breathing, circulation), checking, 120–123
Abdominal thrusts, as first aid for choking, 150, 251
Accident prevention, 50–51
Action
    physical, 26
    taking, 22
Activities for kids, 70, 231–238
    Coffee Filter Butterflies!, 232
    Fancy Fruit Parfaits, 232
    Follow the Leader, 233
    Fruity Play Dough, 234
    Funky Monkey and Very Berry Smoothies, 235
    H.O.R.S.E., 233
    Paper Bowl Jellyfish, 236
    Peanut Butter and Banana Sandwich, 237
    Red Light, Green Light, 238
    Roll the Ball, 237
Activity sheets, 190–209
    AED–Fact or Fiction, 203
    Creating Developmentally Appropriate Play, 197
    Dazed and Confused, 208–209
    FIND a Solution: But My Parents Let Me!, 198–199
    FIND a Solution: Double Trouble, 192–193
    FIND a Solution: Little Picasso, 195–196
    Getting to Know the Family–What Should You Ask?, 191
    I.D. the Consequence, 194
    Memory Challenge–Allergic Reaction, 206
    Memory Challenge–Diapering, 200
    Memory Challenge–External Bleeding, 207
    Team Challenge–Everyday Child Care, 201–202
    Test Your Instincts, 204–205
ADHD. *See* Attention deficit hyperactivity disorder (ADHD)
Adolescents, nutrition and, 87
AED. *See* Automated external defibrillator (AED)
AED–Fact or Fiction activity sheet, 203
Ages of children, ability to handle job and, 10
Airway
    checking, 120, 122
    opening unconscious child's, 277

    recovery positions, 127
    See also Choking
Allergic reactions, 156–157, 206
    to food, 83
    minor, 240
    severe (anaphylaxis), 156–157, 240–241
Anaphylaxis, 156–157, 240–241
Animal bites, 166, 241
Animal droppings, 39
Ankle drag, 130
Apps, preparedness, 44
Aspirin, Reye's syndrome and, 91
Asthma attacks, 148, 241–242
Asthma inhaler, assisting with, 176
Attention deficit hyperactivity disorder (ADHD), 26
Auto-injector, 156
    assisting with, 184
Automated external defibrillator (AED), 136, 139–140
    AED–Fact or Fiction activity, 203
    for child older than 1 year, 260–261
    for child younger than 1 year, 262–263
    cardiac emergencies and, 137
    use of, 146
Axillary temperature, 182

B
Babies. *See* Infants
Back blows, as first aid for choking, 150, 151, 251, 252–253
Back injury, 120, 133, 173–174, 259
Bacteria, 114
Balloons, as safety hazards, 54
Bathing children, 95
    scald burns and, 50–51
Bathing safety, 60
Bed
    putting baby to, 201
    putting children to, 96–97
Bee stings, 163, 242–243
Behavior
    addressing misbehavior, 24–29
    common challenging, 30–33
    encouraging good, 25
    modeling good, 14–15, 19
Bike safety, 72
Bites and stings, 163–166, 241, 242–243, 269–270, 271–272, 273, 275–276
Biting (human), 32
Black widow spider, 164, 165

Blanket drag, 130
Bleeding, 167–169, 207
    minor, 243
    nosebleed, 169, 267–268
    severe, 185, 243–244
Blister, 244
Blood sugar (diabetic) emergency, 157–158, 245
Bone injury, 170–175, 245–246, 265–267
    broken bone, 245–246
Bottle-feeding, 88–89, 104–105
Botulism, honey and, 85
Break-in, home, 36
Breath-holding spells, 30
Breathing, checking, 122–123
Breathing barrier, CPR, 114, 124, 277
Breathing emergencies, 141, 148–152
    prevention of, 230
Brown recluse spider, 164, 165
Bruises, 167–168, 247
Burns
    chemical, 247
    electrical, 248
    first aid for, 169–170
    heat (thermal), 248–249
    prevention of, 50–51, 230
    sun, 249–250
Business aspects of caregiving, 1–15, 224
    building your business, 14–15
    marketing your services, 4–8
Business cards, 4, 9
    sample, 212
Business Card Template, 4

C

Call, emergency, 124–125
Carbon monoxide (CO) detectors, 48
Carbon monoxide (CO) poisoning, 48
Cardiac Chain of Survival, 136–137
Cardiac emergencies, 136–140, 250–253
Cardiopulmonary resuscitation (CPR), 136, 137–139
    breathing barriers, 114, 124, 277
    for breathing emergency, 141
    cardiac emergencies and, 137
    certification in, 2, 12, 57, 116–117
    for child older than 1 year, 138, 142–143, 260
    for infant, 139, 144-145, 252
    hands-only, 139
    performance of, 134
    on unconscious child, 123, 126
Care, emergency, 126–128
Caregiver's Report Record, 15, 227–228
Caregiver's Safety Inspection Checklist, 229–230

Caregiver's Self-Assessment Tool, 3, 10, 213–216
Care routines, 74, 80, 96–97
Car safety, 42–44
Car seat recommendations, 42, 43
Certifications
    caregiving, 9
    CPR, 2, 12, 57, 116–117
    first aid, 2, 12, 116–117
Check
    the child, 118–123
    the scene, 118
CHECK–CALL–CARE, 118–128
Chest, checking injured child's, 131
Chest thrusts, as first aid for choking, 151–152, 253
Child abuse and neglect, 23
Child care
    basic, 222–224
    overnight, 98
    parent expectations for, 2
    skills and qualifications for, 2
    types of jobs, 2–3
Childhelp National Child Abuse Hotline, 23
Children
    checking in emergency, 118–123
    communication with, 121–122
    CPR for, 138–139, 141, 142–143
    picking up and holding, 81–82
    risk for choking, 53–54
    with special needs, 12
    See also Conscious child; Infants; Preschoolers; School-age children; Toddlers; Unconscious child
Choices, limitation of, 20
Choking, 149–152
    common hazards, 55, 85–86
    conscious, 150–151, 177–178, 250–253
    prevention of, 53–54, 230
    unconscious, 141, 151–152, 179–180, 254–256
ChooseMyPlate, 88
Circle of drowning prevention, 57
Circulation, checking, 123
Clothes drag, 130
CO. *See* under Carbon monoxide (CO)
Coffee Filter Butterflies!, 232
Cold-related illness, 161–162, 258, 265
Colic, 78
Communication, 19–20
    with children, 121–122
    positive, 19
Concussion, 174–175
Conscious child
    checking, 119, 131–132
    choking in, 150–151, 177–178, 250–253
    moving, 128–130

Consciousness, loss of, 153
Consequences
    logical, 29, 194
    natural, 29, 194
    time-outs, 29, 194
    withholding privileges, 29, 194
CPR. See Cardiopulmonary resuscitation (CPR)
Cradle hold, 82
Creating Developmentally Appropriate Play activity, 197
Creativity, 21
Cribs, 98
Crying baby
    handling, 77–79
    soothing, 79
Cultural differences, among families, 11
Cup, drinking from, 85
Cuts and scrapes, 168–169

D

Daily care, helping children with, 80
Dazed and Confused activity sheet, 208–209
Decision making, 22
Defibrillation. See Automated external defibrillator (AED)
Diabetic emergency, 157–158, 245
Diapering, 92–93, 108–109, 200
Diarrhea, 153, 155
Digital thermometers, 155
Discipline, 220
Disease transmission, minimization of, 74–77, 114
Dislocations, 171–173
Disposable gloves, 77, 114
    removing, 100
Dog bites, 166
Door, answering home, 35
Dress, appropriate
    for caregiver, 9, 14
    for children, 37
Dressing children, 94
    helping child put on and take off a shirt, 110–111
Drowning
    pools and risk of, 38
    prevention of, 56–59, 230
Drowning hazards, 39

E

Earthquake safety, 47
Electrical shock, prevention of, 51
Embedded object, first aid for, 268
Emergencies, 112–134
    action steps (CHECK–CALL–CARE), 118–128

blood sugar, 157–158, 245
breathing, 141, 148–152
calling for help, 124–126, 128
cardiac, 136–140, 250–253
care, 126–128
checking injured child or infant, 118–123
environmental, 160–166
first aid, 239–277
moving injured child, 128–130
overcoming barriers to act, 113
preparedness for, 113–117
shock, 123
    See also Automated external defibrillator (AED); Cardiopulmonary resuscitation (CPR)
Emergency medical services (EMS), heart emergencies and, 136
Emergency medical technicians (EMTs), 125
Emergency number, calling, 124–125
Emergency preparedness kit, 45
Emergency responders, 125
Emotional development, play and, 63
EMS. See Emergency medical services (EMS)
EMTs. See Emergency medical technicians (EMTs)
Environmental emergencies, 160–166
Epilepsy, 158, 270
Epinephrine Auto-Injector, 156
    assisting with, 184

F

Fainting, 159, 256–257
Fall prevention, 61, 229
Family Emergency Information Card, 12, 116, 117, 225–226
Family income, differences in, 11
Family interview, 8–13
Family Interview Form, 12, 219–224
Family structure, types of, 11
Family values, 11
FAST (face, arm, speech, time) check, 275
Fear, acting in emergency and, 113
Febrile seizures, 156, 257–258
Feedback
    from family, 15
    positive, 21
Feeding children, 83–90
Fees, child care, 13
Feet, checking injured child's, 131
Fever, 153, 155–156, 257–258
    defined, 156
FIND a Solution
    But My Parents Let Me!, 198–199
    Double Trouble, 192–193
    Little Picasso, 195–196

FIND decision-making model, 22, 192–193, 195–196, 198–199
Fire, house, 48–49
Fire extinguishers, 49
First aid, 147–189
    for breathing emergencies, 148–152
    certification in, 116–117
    for choking, 150–152
    for environmental emergencies, 160–166
    for injuries to muscles, bones and joints, 170–175
    skill sheets, 176–189
    for soft tissue injuries, 167–170
    for sudden illness, 153–160
First aid emergencies, 239–277
First aid kit, 114, 116
    putting together, 117
First impressions, 9
Flossing, 95–96
Follow the Leader activity, 233
Food
    allergies to, 83
    as choking hazards, 55
Food poisoning, prevention of, 84
Forms, sample, 210–230
    Caregiver's Assessment Tool, 213–216
    Caregiver's Report Record, 227–228
    Caregiver's Safety Inspection Checklist, 229–230
    Family Emergency Information Card, 225–226
    Family Interview Form, 219–224
    Parental Consent and Contact Form, 217–218
    Sample Business Card, 212
    Sample Résumé, 211
Fractures, 171–173, 245–246
Frostbite, 162, 258
Fruit Parfaits, Fancy, 232
Funky Monkey Smoothie, 235

G
Games. See Activities for kids
Germ transmission, prevention of, 74–77, 114
Getting to Know the Family—What Should You Ask?, 191
Ground rules, 21, 22
Gunfire, staying safe if you hear, 41

H
Hand sanitizer, 75, 77
Hand washing, 74, 75–76, 99, 114
Head, checking injured child's, 132
Headache, 153
Head injury, 120, 133, 173–174, 259
    concussion, 174–175

Head-tilt/chin lift maneuver, 120, 122
Heart emergency. See Cardiac emergency
Heat cramps, 160, 263, 264
Heat exhaustion, 160–161, 263, 264
Heat-related illness, 160–161, 263–265
Heat stroke, 43, 161, 263–264
Hitting, 32
Hives, 156
Hobo spider, 164, 165
Home electronic security system, 35
Honey, infants and, 85, 89
H.O.R.S.E. game, 233
Hot tub safety, 56
Household items/objects
    as choking hazards, 55
    poisonous, 60
Household routines, 22
Household rules, 12, 220
Humor, in communication, 20
Hygiene basics, 202
Hyperventilation, 58
Hypothermia, 161–162, 265

I
I.D. the Consequence activity sheet, 194
Illnesses
    cold-related, 161–162
    heat-related, 160–161
    sudden, 153–160
Infants
    behavior of, 28
    checking unconscious, 133
    communication with, 121
    conscious choking in, 151–152, 178, 252–253
    CPR for, 139, 144–145
    crying, 77–79, 202
    daily care for, 80
    dressing, 94
    feeding, 85–86
    fever in, 156
    heart emergency in, 261–263
    holding, 102
    performing CPR on, 134
    picking up and holding, 81–82, 101
    play and, 66
    risk of heat stroke if left in car and, 43–44
    safe sleep for, 98
    safety and, 52
    sunscreen and, 38
    unconscious choking in, 180–181, 255–256
    vomiting or diarrhea in, 154
Injuries, prevention of accidental, 50–51

Insect bites, 39, 163–164, 269–270, 273, 275–276

Internet, safety tips for, 5

J

Joint injury, 170–174, 265–267

K

Kicking, 32

Kitchen, prevention of fires in, 49

L

Leader, definition of, 17

Leadership, 16–33

    addressing misbehavior, 24–29

    democratic, 18, 21

    directive, 18

    empathetic, 18

    "hands-off," 17

    skills for, 19–22

    styles of, 17–18

Learn-to-Swim classes, 58

Legs, checking injured child's, 131

Lifeguards, 59

Lightning, safety and, 46

Listening, 20

M

Marketing caregiving services, 4–8

Meal planning, 84–88, 201

Medications, giving child, 60, 61, 90–91

Memory Challenge!

    Allergic Reaction, 206

    Diapering, 200

    External Bleeding, 207

Mental development, play and, 63

Military families, caregiving for, 5

Milk intake

    preschoolers and, 87

    toddlers and, 86

Misbehavior, addressing, 24–29

Mobile devices

    9-1-1 calls on, 125

    driving and, 43

    use of, 14, 51

Morning routines, 97–98, 202

Motivation, 21

Moving injured child, 128–130

Muscle injury, 170–174, 265–267

MyPlate Kids' Place, 88

N

Naps, 96

National Poison Control Center Hotline, 159–160, 269

Nausea, 153

Neck, checking injured child's, 132

Neck injury, 120, 133, 173–174, 259

Networking, as source of jobs, 4

Northwestern brown (hobo) spider, 164, 165

Nosebleed, 169, 267–268

Number of children, ability to handle job and, 10

Nutrition, 84–87

O

Object, embedded, 268

Online caregiving services, 7–8

Oral temperature, 183

Overnight child care, 98

P

Pack-strap carry, 129

Paper Bowl Jellyfish activity, 236

Paramedics, 125

Parental Consent and Contact Form, 12, 90, 115, 217–218

Parents

    emergency preparedness and, 115–116

    expectations for caregiver, 2

    feeding children and preferences of, 83–84

Park, safety at, 71

PASS method, for fire extinguisher use, 49

Payment details, 13

Peanut Butter and Banana Sandwich, 237

Pets, 12, 15

Phone, answering home, 35–36

Physical development, play and, 63

Plan, disaster preparedness, 45

Plants, poisonous, 39

Plastic bags, as safety hazards, 54

Play, 62–72

    active, 64

    child development and, 63

    constructive, 64

    creating developmentally appropriate, 197

    fantasy, 64

    how to, with children, 65–70

    quiet, 64

    safety and, 71–72, 220–222

    social, 64

    See also Activities for kids

Play Dough, Fruity, 234

Playground safety, 71

Poisoning
  first aid for, 159–160, 268–269
  food, 84
  plants and, 39
  prevention of, 59–60, 229
Pool safety, 38, 56, 58–59
  at public pools, 58–59
Potty-training, 92, 93, 201
Preparation
  for caregiving job, 14, 21
  for house fire, 48
  for weather events, 44, 45
Preschoolers
  activities for, 232–238
  behavior of, 28
  communication with, 121
  daily care for, 80
  dressing, 94
  feeding, 85, 87
  play and, 68
  safety and, 52
Privileges, withholding, 29, 194

R
Rabies, 166
Rates, child care, 13
Record keeping, 15
Recovery positions, 127
Red Light, Green Light, 238
References, 2, 6–7
Reliability, 14
Religious beliefs, family, 11
Rescue inhalers, 148
  assisting with, 176
Responsibilities, of caregiving job, 10
Résumé, 6–7, 9
  sample, 211
Résumé Builder Tool, 6
Reye's syndrome, 91
RICE (rest, immobilize, cold, elevate) method, 171–172, 266
Roll the Ball activity, 237
Routine care, 201–202
Rules
  ground, 21, 22
  household, 12, 220
Rural safety, 40

S
Safety, 34–61
  caregiver, 7

Caregiver's Safety Inspection Checklist, 229–230
  from house fires, 48–49
  outdoor, 39
  play and, 71–72, 220–222
  powers of observation and, 40
  weather events and, 44–47
  while away from the house, 39–41
  while driving, 42–44
  while in the home, 35–36
  while out and about, 37–44
  in the yard, 37–38
Safety Checklist, 50
Safety net, 44
School-age children
  ability to follow rules, 28
  activities for, 232–238
  communication with, 122
  daily care for, 80
  feeding, 87
  older, 28, 53, 69, 80
  play and, 69
  safety and, 52–53
  temper tantrums and, 31
  younger, 28, 52, 69, 80
Scooter safety, 72
Scorpion, 165
Scorpion stings, 164, 165, 269–270
Scrapes, 168–169
Seizures, 153, 158–159, 270
  febrile, 156, 257–258
Self-assessment, 3, 10, 213–216
Shaken baby injuries, 78
Shock, 123, 271
Shoulder hold, 81
Shoulders, checking injured child's, 132
Sibling rivalry, 32–33
SIDS. See Sudden infant death syndrome (SIDS)
Skateboard safety, 72
Skill sheets
  applying an anatomic splint, 188
  applying a rigid splint, 187
  applying a sling, 189
  applying a soft splint, 186
  assisting with an asthma inhaler, 176
  assisting with an epinephrine auto-injector, 184
  bottle-feeding, 104–105
  checking a conscious child, 131–132
  checking an unconscious child, 133–134
  conscious choking–child (older than 1 year), 177
  conscious choking–infant, 178
  controlling severe bleeding, 185
  CPR–child, 142–143

CPR–infant, 144–145
diapering, 108–109
hand washing, 99
helping a child put on and take off a shirt, 110–111
holding an infant, 102
picking up and holding a toddler, 103
picking up an infant, 101
removing disposable gloves, 100
spoon-feeding, 106–107
taking a temperature, 182–183
unconscious choking–child, 179
unconscious choking–infant, 180–181
using an AED, 146
Sleep, for babies, 98
Sleep routines, 96
Slings, 266–267
applying, 189
Smoke alarms, 48
Smoothies, Funky Monkey and Very Berry, 235
Snacks
balanced, 87–88
serving older children, 90
Snake bites, 271–272
venomous, 272–273
Social development, play and, 63
Social media, concerns about use of, 3, 36
Soft-tissue injuries, 167–170
Spacers, rescue inhalers and, 148, 176
Spider bites, 39, 164, 273
Spinal injury, 133, 173–174, 259
Splinter, 274
Splinting/splints, 172–173, 266–267
anatomic, 173, 188, 266
rigid, 187, 266
soft, 186, 266
Spoon-feeding, 89, 106–107
Sprains, 171–173
Stairs, fall prevention and, 61
Standard precautions, germ transmission and, 114
Stings, bites and, 163–166, 241, 242–243,
    269–270, 271–272, 275–276
Stomach, checking injured child's, 131
Stomachaches, 153, 154
Stomach troubles, 154–155
Strains, 171–173
Stranger safety, 35–36, 39–41
Strangulation, prevention of, 54–56
Stroke, 274–275
heat, 161
Sudden infant death syndrome (SIDS), 98
Suffocation, prevention of, 54–56
Sunburn, 249–250

Sun safety, 38
Sunscreen, 38
Swimming safety, 57–58
in public pool, 58–59
See also Drowning

T

Team Challenge–Everyday Child Care, 201–202
Temperature, taking a child's, 155–156, 182–183
Temper tantrums, 30–32
Temporal temperature, 182
Temporal thermometers, 155
Test Your Instincts activity sheet, 204–205
Thunderstorms, safety and, 46
Tick bites, 163–164, 275–276
Time-out, 29, 194
Toddlers
activities for, 233, 235, 237
behavior of, 28
communication with, 121
daily care for, 80
dressing, 94
feeding, 86
picking up and holding, 82, 103
play and, 67
safety and, 52
Tooth, knocked out, 276
Tooth brushing, 95–96
Tornado safety, 47
Toys
as choking hazards, 55
for infants, 66
for preschoolers, 68
for school-age children, 69
for toddlers, 67
with wheels, safety and, 72
Transportation, to and from job, 8, 10
Triangular bandages, 173, 266–267
Tripping hazards, 39
Two-person seat carry, 129
Tympanic temperature, 182
Tympanic thermometers, 155

U

Unconscious child
checking, 120–123, 133–134, 276–277
choking in, 152, 179–181, 254–256
moving, 128–130
recovery positions, 127
Upset stomach, 153

V

Very Berry Smoothies, 235
Viruses, 114
Vision, problems with, 153
Vomiting, 153, 154

W

Waking children up, 97–98
Walking assist, 129
Water, amount to drink, 88
Water Safety classes, 58
Water safety training, 2
Websites, online caregiving, 5, 7–8
Wound prevention, 229